Analysing financial performance

Workbook

KT-415-797

Aubrey Penning

© Aubrey Penning, 2013. Reprinted 2014.

All rights reserved. No part of this publication may be reproduced, stored in a retrieval system, or transmitted in any form or by any means, electronic, mechanical, photo-copying, recording or otherwise, without the prior consent of the copyright owners, or in accordance with the provisions of the Copyright, Designs and Patents Act 1988, or under the terms of any licence permitting limited copying issued by the Copyright Licensing Agency, Saffron House, 6-10 Kirby Street, London EC1N 8TS.

Published by Osborne Books Limited
Unit 1B Everoak Estate
Bromyard Road, Worcester WR2 5HP
Tel 01905 748071
Email books@osbornebooks.co.uk
Website www.osbornebooks.co.uk

Design by Laura Ingham

Printed by CPI Group (UK) Limited, Croydon, CR0 4YY, on environmentally friendly, acid-free paper from managed forests.

British Library Cataloguing in Publication Data
A catalogue record for this book is available from the British Library

ISBN 978 1909173 309

Contents

Introduction

Chapter activities

Chapter activities – answers

Practice assessments – tasks

Practice assessments – answers

Acknowledgements

The authors wish to thank the following for their help with the production of the book: Jon Moore and Cathy Turner. Thanks are also due to Lynn Watkins for her technical editing and to Laura Ingham for her designs for this new series.

The publisher is indebted to the Association of Accounting Technicians for its help and advice to our author and editors during the preparation of this text.

Author

Aubrey Penning has many years experience of teaching accountancy on a variety of courses in Worcester and Gwent. He is a Certified Accountant, and before his move into full-time teaching he worked for the health service, a housing association and a chemical supplier. Until recently he was the AAT course coordinator at Worcester College of Technology, specialising in the areas of management accounting and taxation.

Introduction

what this book covers

This book has been written to cover the 'Financial performance' Unit which is mandatory for the revised (2013) AAT Level 4 Diploma in Accounting.

what this book contains

This book is set out in two sections:

- **Chapter Activities** which provide extra practice material in addition to the activities included in the Osborne Books Tutorial text. Answers to the Chapter activities are included in this book.

- **Practice Assessments** are provided to prepare the student for the Computer Based Assessments. They are based directly on the structure, style and content of the sample assessment material provided by the AAT at www.aat.org.uk. Suggested answers to the Practice Assessments are set out in this book.

further information

If you want to know more about our products and resources, please visit www.osbornebooks.co.uk for further details and access to our online shop.

Chapter activities

1 Management accounting techniques

1.1 The table below contains the last three months' cost per kilogram for product Alpha.

January	February	March
Actual price was £20.40	Actual price was £19.20	Actual price was £21.00
Seasonal variation was +£1.20	Seasonal variation was −£0.30	Seasonal variation was +£1.20

The trend in prices is an increase of £ [ ] per month.

1.2 A company has provided the following information:

	January	February	March
Total cost	£150,000	£168,000	£225,000
Total quantity purchased	10,000 kg	10,500 kg	12,500 kg

The cost index for March based upon January being the base period of 100 is:

		✔
(a)	150	
(b)	125	
(c)	120	
(d)	83	

1.3 The cost per unit of a product has increased from £50 in January to £54 in April. The cost per unit was £40 when the index was rebased to 100.

✔

(a) The cost index in April was 135 and the increase from January to April is 8.0%	
(b) The cost index in April was 108 and the increase from January to April is 8.0%	
(c) The cost index in April is 125 and the increase from January to April is 35.0%	
(d) The cost index in April is 135 and the increase from January to April is 4.0%	

1.4 Analyse the following features based on whether they apply to marginal costing or absorption costing by ticking the appropriate column in the table.

✔

Feature	Marginal Costing	Absorption Costing
Can be used to set a minimum selling price	✓	
Complies with standard IAS 2 for inventory valuation		✓
Can be used for planning and control but is of limited use for decision making		✓
Can be used in conjunction with break even analysis	✓	
Can be used in conjunction with 'full cost plus' pricing		✓
Is often used in conjunction with discounted cash flow decision making techniques	✓	

1.5   Avid Greene is considering installing a rainwater recycling system in his house. The system will cost £8,000 to purchase and install. The system would result in an annual saving of £200 in water charges. Avid intends to sell his house in 5 years, and estimates that having a rainwater recycling system will add £5,000 to the sale proceeds of the house. Avid's cost of capital is 10%, and this rate has been used for the discount factors in the table shown below.

(a)   Complete the following table to calculate the net present value of the system.

Year	Detail	Cash Flow £	Discount Factor	Present Value £
0	Purchase and Installation		1.000	
1	Savings and increased house sale proceeds		0.909	
2			0.826	
3			0.751	
4			0.683	
5			0.621	
Net Present Value				

(b)   Complete the following sentence.

The net present value of the scheme is **positive / negative** so from a financial point of view the scheme is **worthwhile / not worthwhile**.

1.6   The costs for a product have been calculated as follows based on two possible production levels:

Volume of production	10,000 units	18,000 units
Total cost	£100,000	£152,000

Costs are either fixed or variable.

Using the high-low method, estimate the total fixed costs and the variable costs per unit.

1.7   The costs for a product have been calculated as follows based on two possible production levels:

Volume of production	22,000 units	28,000 units
Total cost	£500,000	£606,000

It has been established that the fixed cost element contains a step of £40,000 when volume exceeds 26,000 units. Other costs are variable.

Using the high-low method, estimate the total stepped fixed costs at each production level and the variable costs per unit.

2   Standard costing – direct costs

2.1   A company purchases 12,000 kilograms of material at a cost of £37,800. The standard cost per kilogram is £3.20. The total material price variance is:

	✔
(a) £0.05 Adverse	
(b) £0.05 Favourable	
(c) £600 Adverse	
(d) £600 Favourable	

2.2   A company used 15,000 kilograms of material at a cost of £37,500. The production was 1000 units, for which the standard usage is 14,500 kilograms of material at a total standard cost of £37,700. The material usage variance is:

	✔
(a) 500 kilograms Adverse	
(b) £1,300 Adverse	
(c) £1,250 Adverse	
(d) £200 Favourable	

2.3   A company expects to produce 18,000 units of Z using 6,000 labour hours. The standard cost of labour is £15 per hour. If the actual output is 17,500 units, what is the standard labour cost for this output?

	✔
(a) £87,500	
(b) £90,000	
(c) £787,500	
(d) £810,000	

2.4 Radnor Ltd manufactures heating equipment. The company has several divisions including the Radiators Division. You work as an Accounting Technician reporting to the Finance Director.

The Radiators Division operates a standard cost system in which:

- Purchases of materials are recorded at standard cost

- Direct material and direct labour costs are variable

- Production overheads are fixed and absorbed on a labour hours basis

The budgeted activity and actual results for the month of November 20-3 are as follows:

	Budget		Actual	
Production units (radiators)		10,000		11,500
Direct materials (paint)	500 litres	£2,500	650 litres	£3,120
Direct material (sheet steel)	30,000 sq metres	£45,000	35,000 sq metres	£51,200
Direct labour	4,000 hours	£48,000	4,100 hours	£51,250
Fixed overheads		£120,000		£120,000
Total cost		£215,500		£225,570

Calculate the following variances for November:

Variance	£	A/F
Direct material (paint) price variance		
Direct material (sheet steel) usage variance		
Direct labour rate variance		
Direct labour efficiency variance		

2.5   A material actually costs £15,400 for 11,500 kg. This results in a favourable material price variance of £700.

All the 11,500 kg purchased were used to make 24,000 units. This resulted in a favourable material usage variance of £700.

(a)   The standard material cost per kg is   £

(b)   The standard quantity of material to make one unit is   kg

(c)   The standard cost of the materials to make one unit is   £

2.6   The direct labour efficiency variance has been accurately calculated for the production of 2,000 units in week 9 as £450 Adverse.

The production took 445 hours. The labour standard time to make one unit is 12 minutes.

The standard time to make 2,000 units is   hours.

The standard labour rate is   £   per hour.

2.7   The actual cost of 5,500 hours of direct labour is £59,400. The direct labour rate variance is £1,100 favourable.

The standard hourly rate is   £   per hour.

2.8 The standard direct material cost is based on using 0.5 kilos of material at £65 per kilo for every unit manufactured.

3,000 units were manufactured, using 1,560 kilos of material with a total cost of £99,840.

Prepare a reconciliation of the budgeted material cost with the actual material cost using the following table.

Budgeted / Standard cost of materials for actual production			£
Variances:	**Favourable £**	**Adverse £**	
Direct material price			
Direct material usage			
Total variance			£
Actual cost of materials for actual production			£

2.9 The standard direct labour time is based on taking 6 hours to make each 100 manufactured units. The standard labour rate is £12.50 per hour.

5,000 units were manufactured, taking 307 labour hours with a total cost of £3,945.

Prepare a reconciliation of the budgeted labour cost with the actual labour cost using the following table.

Budgeted / Standard cost of labour for actual production			£
Variances:	**Favourable £**	**Adverse £**	
Direct labour rate			
Direct labour efficiency			
Total variance			£
Actual cost of labour for actual production			£

3   Standard costing – variable and fixed overheads

3.1   The following information has been calculated for the production of 1 unit of Zed:

- Each unit will require 12 kilograms of material at a cost of £8.50 per kilogram
- Each unit will require 0.6 hours of labour at a total cost of £9
- Fixed overheads total £200,000 and the estimated output will be 2,500 units of Zed
- Fixed overheads are absorbed on a per unit basis

Complete the standard cost card below.

1 unit of Zed	Quantity	Cost per unit £	Total cost £
Material			
Labour			
Fixed costs			
Total			

3.2   You have been given the following information:

- Budgeted fixed overheads are £700,000
- Budgeted output is 35,000 units
- Actual output is 30,000 units
- Actual fixed overheads are £680,000

The fixed overhead volume variance is £ [   ]   **favourable / adverse**.

The fixed overhead expenditure variance is £ [   ]   **favourable / adverse**.

3.3 You have been given the following information:

- Budgeted fixed overheads are £80,000
- Budgeted output is 10,000 units and 5,000 labour hours
- Actual output is 8,000 units and 4,300 actual labour hours
- Actual fixed overheads are £85,000

The fixed overhead efficiency variance is £ [   ] favourable / adverse.

The fixed overhead capacity variance is £ [   ] favourable / adverse.

3.4 You have been given the following information:

- Budgeted fixed overheads are £120,000
- Budgeted output is 12,000 units and 4,000 labour hours
- Actual output is 11,400 units and 3,950 actual labour hours
- Actual fixed overheads are £118,000

Complete the following table to show the fixed overhead variances.

	Variance £	A / F	Variance £	A / F
Expenditure Variance				
Capacity Variance				
Efficiency Variance				
Volume Variance				
Total Fixed Overhead Variances				

3.5 Complete the following table by ticking the relevant column to show whether each statement is true or false.

✔

	True	False
(a) The fixed overhead volume variance will always be numerically equal and opposite to the fixed overhead expenditure variance		
(b) The fixed overhead capacity variance together with the fixed overhead efficiency variance will always equal the fixed overhead volume variance		
(c) Adverse variances will be credited to the statement of profit or loss, while favourable variances will be debited		
(d) The net total of the fixed overhead expenditure variance and the fixed overhead volume variance is the amount of under or over absorption of fixed overheads		
(e) If fixed overheads are absorbed on a per unit basis then neither the fixed overhead capacity or efficiency variances can be calculated in the normal way		
(f) If fixed overheads are absorbed on a direct labour hour basis, then the fixed overhead capacity and efficiency variances will relate to the utilisation of direct labour		

3.6 You have been given the following information:

- Fixed overheads are budgeted at £430,000
- Output is budgeted at 344,000 units
- Fixed overheads are absorbed on a per unit basis
- Actual fixed overheads amount to £419,500
- Actual output is 350,000 units

Prepare a reconciliation of budgeted fixed overheads with actual fixed overheads using fixed overhead variances in the following table.

Budgeted / Standard fixed cost for actual production			£
Variances:	Favourable £	Adverse £	
Fixed overhead expenditure			
Fixed overhead volume			
Total variance			£
Actual fixed cost for actual production			£

3.7 A company uses direct labour hours to charge variable overheads. The standard industry labour hours per unit produced is 0.5 hours, and the standard hourly charge is £3.50. During the month 10,500 units were produced, using 5,400 direct labour hours. The actual variable overheads for the month were £19,100.

Required:

Calculate:

(a)   the variable overhead expenditure variance

(b)   the variable overhead efficiency variance

3.8 A company uses machine hours to charge variable overheads. The standard units produced per machine hour are 10, and the total standard variable overhead cost per unit is £1.30.

During the month 20,250 units were produced, using 1,990 machine hours. The actual variable overheads for the month were £27,600.

Required:

Calculate:

(a)   the variable overhead expenditure variance

(b)   the variable overhead efficiency variance

4 Standard costing – further analysis

4.1 ✓ A company bottles cleaning fluid which is sold in two-litre plastic bottles.

The following budgetary control report has been provided:

	Budget		**Actual**	
Production (bottles)		10,000		10,500
Liquid cleaner	20,000 litres	£25,000	21,100 litres	£25,400
Plastic bottles	10,000 units	£2,000	10,800 units	£2,064
Direct labour	200 hours	£3,300	230 hours	£3,625
Fixed overheads		£7,000		£7,500
Total cost		£37,300		£38,589

The following variances have been accurately calculated, although for some it is not known whether they are adverse or favourable:

Fixed overhead expenditure	£500
Direct materials (liquid cleaner) price	£975 F
Direct materials (bottles) price	£96 F
Direct materials (liquid cleaner) usage	£125 A
Direct materials (bottles) usage	£60
Direct labour rate	£170
Direct labour efficiency	£330 A
Fixed overhead volume	£350 F

Complete the operating statement on the next page, including the budgeted cost for the 10,500 units of production and the variances. Make sure that the total agrees with the actual cost of production.

Budgeted cost for actual production			£
Variances:	**Favourable £**	**Adverse £**	
Direct materials (liquid cleaner) price			
Direct materials (liquid cleaner) usage			
Direct materials (bottles) price			
Direct materials (bottles) usage			
Direct labour rate			
Direct labour efficiency			
Fixed overhead expenditure			
Fixed overhead volume			
Total variances			£
Actual cost of actual production			£

4.2 Aye Limited uses Standard Costing to manage its costs, and absorbs fixed overheads using direct labour hours as an absorption base. It makes one product, and each unit takes five standard direct labour hours to manufacture.

Standard Direct Costs for one unit are:

- Direct Material 3 litres at £4.00 per litre = £12.00 per unit

- Direct Labour 5 hours at £10 per hour = £50.00 per unit

- Fixed Overheads 5 hours at £50 per hour = £250.00 per unit

The standard fixed overheads for one month are £62,500. The standard production output for one month is 1,250 standard hours (i.e. 250 units of product). This gave a budgeted standard absorption rate of £50 per standard direct labour hour as shown above.

During February, actual production was 1,300 standard direct labour hours (i.e. 260 units of product).

Actual Costs for February were as follows:

- Direct Material 800 litres, costing a total of £3,120

- Direct Labour 1,340 hours, costing a total of £14,000

- Fixed Overheads actual cost £64,800

Calculate and insert all the variances listed in the following table. Use the table to reconcile the budgeted cost of actual production with the actual cost.

Budgeted cost for actual production			£
Variances:	**Favourable £**	**Adverse £**	
Direct materials price			
Direct materials usage			
Direct labour rate			
Direct labour efficiency			
Fixed overhead expenditure			
Fixed overhead capacity			
Fixed overhead efficiency			
Total variances			£
Actual cost of actual production			£

4.3 A company uses material M in its production of product P. Material M has a standard price of £20 per kilo, and a standard usage of 10 kilos per unit of P.

In June, 1,500 units of P were made, using 14,880 kilos of material M.

Since the standards were originally set the specification for manufacturing product P has been amended, resulting in 3% less quantity of material M being required in each unit.

Complete the following table to show the direct material usage variance, and its analysis into the part caused by the change in product specification and the remainder.

Direct Material Usage Variance			Part of variance caused by change in product specification			Part of variance caused by unknown factors		
	£	A / F		£	A / F		£	A / F

4.4 Chippum Limited makes frozen potato chips from raw potatoes that are purchased from UK farms. The potatoes are first machine washed, and then put through a peeling and slicing machine where the chips are cut to shape. At this stage a quality check is carried out by staff who manually pick out from the conveyor system and discard any chips that have blemishes. The chips are then cooked, frozen and bagged ready for sale.

The company operates a standard costing system, and in September the following variances were recorded.

Variance	Adverse £	Favourable £
Direct material (potato) price variance	5,500	
Direct material (potato) usage variance	9,300	
Direct labour rate variance	1,200	
Direct labour efficiency variance	5,600	
Fixed overhead expenditure variance	1,000	
Fixed overhead volume variance	7,400	

The following information has been obtained about the operations during September.

- The recent weather has resulted in a poor potato harvest in the UK. The consequences include higher prices due to shortages as well as poorer quality potatoes with more blemishes than usual.

- The manual quality control operation involved increased hours and overtime working.

- The conveyor system was slowed to enable the more intensive quality control, and this caused mechanical problems, resulting in a break down which lasted several hours. A contractor was used to supply and fit the necessary replacement parts.

Write an email to the Production Director that suggests possible reason(s) for each of the variances, based on the information provided.

Email
To:
From:
Date:
Subject:

4.5 A company uses standard marginal costing to monitor and control its costs. The company's only product is a high energy drink which is purchased in bulk and sold in 500ml cans. The drink, cans, direct labour and variable overheads are all variable costs. Fixed overheads are the only fixed costs.

The following budgetary control report has been provided:

	Budget		Actual	
Production (cans)		6,000,000		5,850,000
Drink	3,000,000 litres	£630,000	2,930,000 litres	£644,600
Cans	6,000,000 units	£240,000	5,855,000 units	£234,200
Direct labour	3,000 hours	£36,000	2,900 hours	£34,500
Variable overheads	3,000 hours	£21,000	2,900 hours	£20,700
Fixed overheads		£200,000		£203,500
Total costs		£1,127,000		£1,137,500

Calculate all the variances required and use them to complete the following operating statement.

Budgeted / Standard variable cost for actual production			£
Budgeted fixed costs			£
Variances:	Favourable £	Adverse £	
Direct materials (drink) price			
Direct materials (drink) usage			
Direct materials (cans) price			
Direct materials (cans) usage			
Direct labour rate			
Direct labour efficiency			
Variable overhead expenditure			
Variable overhead efficiency			
Fixed overhead expenditure			
Total variance			£
Actual cost of actual production			£

5   Measuring quality

5.1   Bullseye Limited uses target costing when developing new products. A new product is being considered which has the following cost and revenue information.

Sales	the demand is expected to average 5,000 units per month at a selling price of £7.00 per unit
Materials	the product requires 0.5 kg of material T for each unit
Labour	each unit requires 6 minutes of labour at £14 per hour
Overheads	the product would be manufactured in a separate factory, with total fixed production overheads of £10,000 per month
Profit	the gross margin required is at least 25%

Complete the following table.

Maximum production cost per unit	£
Build up of maximum production cost per unit:	
Materials	£
Labour	£
Overheads	£
Maximum cost per kilo for material T	£

5.2   Delta Limited will be replacing some vans in the next year and needs to decide whether to purchase or lease the vehicles.

The discount factors you will need are shown below.

Year	Discount factor	Year	Discount factor
0	1.00	3	0.864
1	0.952	4	0.823
2	0.907		

(a)   Calculate the discounted lifecycle cost of purchasing each van based upon the following:

- Purchase price of £15,000
- Maintenance costs of £800 for each of the next four years, paid annually in arrears
- A residual value of £4,000 at the end of the four years

Year	0	1	2	3	4
Cash flow					
Discount factor					
Present value					
Net present cost					

(b)   Calculate the discounted lifecycle cost of leasing each van for four years based upon the total annual costs of £4,100 paid annually in advance. This figure includes maintenance. There is no residual value if leased.

Year	0	1	2	3	4
Lease costs					
Discount factor					
Present value					
Net present cost					

(c)   Based on the calculations it is best to **purchase / lease** each van, which saves a net present amount of

£ [   ]

5.3 Delta Limited is considering designing a new product, and will use target costing to arrive at the target cost of the product. You have been given the following information and asked to calculate the target cost for materials so that the purchasing manager can use this as a target in her negotiations with suppliers.

- The price at which the product will be sold is £40

- The company has firm orders for 10,000 units at a price of £40 for the first year

- The fixed costs are £120,000 per year

- The labour requirement is 20 minutes at a cost of £18 per hour

- The required profit margin is 45%

- The material requirement is 200 grams per unit

(a) Calculate the target cost per kilogram for the materials component of the product, using the following table.

	£
Sales price per unit	
Profit margin	
Total costs	
Fixed cost per unit	
Labour cost per unit	
Maximum material cost per unit	
Target cost per kilogram	

(b) Complete the following statement:

The trade price quoted on the supplier's price list is £25 per kilogram. The purchasing manager has negotiated a discount of 15%. The discount should be **accepted / rejected** because the £25 reduces to £_____ which is **above / below** the Target cost.

(c) The minimum percentage discount needed to achieve the Target cost is _____ %

5.4 Analyse each of the following cost examples into the four main groups of the cost of quality by ticking the appropriate columns.

✔

	Prevention Costs	Appraisal Costs	Internal Failure Costs	External Failure Costs
Production staff training costs				
Costs of customer complaints section				
Costs of re-inspection of reworked products				
Inspection of work in progress				
Testing of finished goods				
Loss of customer goodwill				
Customer compensation payments				

6 Measuring performance

6.1 Complete the following table by selecting a valid method of calculation for each ratio.

Ratio Title	Calculation
(a) Gross profit margin	**1** $\dfrac{\text{Sales}}{(\text{All Assets} - \text{Current Liabilities})}$
(b) Debt to equity ratio	**2** $\dfrac{\text{Advertising Costs}}{\text{Sales}} \times 100$
(c) Operating profit margin	**3** $\dfrac{\text{Current Assets}}{\text{Current Liabilities}}$
(d) Return on capital employed	**4** $\dfrac{\text{Trade Receivables}}{\text{Credit Sales}} \times 365$
(e) Advertising cost as a percentage of turnover	**5** $\dfrac{(\text{Total debt} + \text{Preference Share Capital})}{\text{Total Capital Employed}} \times 100$
(f) Asset turnover	**6** $\dfrac{(\text{Current Assets} - \text{Inventory})}{\text{Current Liabilities}}$
(g) Gearing ratio	**7** $\dfrac{\text{Gross Profit}}{\text{Sales}} \times 100$
(h) Current ratio	**8** $\dfrac{\text{Profit before interest}}{\text{Capital Employed}} \times 100$
(i) Receivables' payment period in days	**9** $\dfrac{\text{Profit before interest}}{\text{Sales}} \times 100$
(j) Quick ratio	**10** $\dfrac{(\text{Total debt} + \text{Preference Share Capital}) \times 100}{(\text{Ordinary Share Capital} + \text{Reserves})}$

6.2   A trading company has the following results:

Statement of profit or loss for the year ended 31 December				
	20-8		20-7	
	£	£	£	£
Sales		209,000		196,000
less cost of sales:				
Opening Inventory	24,000		25,000	
Purchases	155,000		150,000	
Closing Inventory	22,000		24,000	
		157,000		151,000
Gross Profit		52,000		45,000
Depreciation	9,000		9,000	
Sundry Expenses	14,000		11,000	
		23,000		20,000
Operating Profit		29,000		25,000
Interest		2,000		2,000
Net Profit		27,000		23,000
Taxation		10,000		10,000
Net Profit after taxation		17,000		13,000
Ordinary Dividends	6,000		5,000	
Preference Dividends	2,000		2,000	
		8,000		7,000
Retained Profit		9,000		6,000

Statement of Financial Position	As at 31/12/20-8	As at 31/12/20-7
	£	£
Non-current Assets	130,000	139,000
Current Assets:		
Inventory	22,000	24,000
Trade Receivables	40,000	36,000
Bank	12,000	5,000
	74,000	65,000
Current Liabilities:		
Trade Payables	46,000	45,000
Short term loans	0	20,000
Net Current Assets	28,000	0
Total Assets less Current Liabilities	158,000	139,000
Non-current Liabilities:		
5% secured loan stock	40,000	40,000
	118,000	99,000
Ordinary Share Capital (50p shares)	35,000	35,000
8% Preference Shares (£1 shares)	25,000	25,000
Share Premium Account	17,000	17,000
Revaluation Reserve	10,000	0
Retained Earnings	31,000	22,000
	118,000	99,000

Complete the following table to show the performance indicators listed for each year. Show the solutions to two decimal places, with the exception of those measured in days which should be rounded to the nearest day.

	20-8	20-7
Gross Profit %		
Return on Capital Employed %		
Operating Profit as % Sales		
Current Ratio		
Asset Turnover		
Quick Ratio		
Trade Receivables Days		
Trade Payables Days		
Gearing Ratio %		

6.3   The performance indicators shown in the following table have been calculated for a trading company. Match the comments on performance shown with the appropriate measure of performance.

Performance Indicator	20-8	20-7	Comments
Gross Profit %	24.88	22.96	The profit before interest as a percentage of turnover has increased in the later year
Return on Capital Employed %	18.35	17.99	There is less value of sales compared to total resources in the later year
Operating Profit as % Sales	13.88	12.76	The profit as a percentage of sales (after taking into account just the cost of sales) has improved from the first year to the second
Current Ratio	1.61	1.00	Credit customers are taking slightly longer on average to pay in the later year than they were in the previous year
Asset Turnover	1.32	1.41	There are more current assets compared to current liabilities in the later year
Quick Ratio	1.13	0.63	The operating profit as a percentage of total resources has increased from year to year
Trade Receivables Days	70	67	A smaller proportion of the capital employed is based on fixed interest capital in the later year
Trade Payables Days	108	158	After excluding inventory, there are more current assets compared to current liabilities in the later year
Gearing Ratio %	41.14	46.76	The company is paying its credit suppliers considerably more quickly in the later year

6.4 Utoxx Limited has developed a potion which claims to detoxify individuals. The product competes with those from several other companies. Meetox is a major competitor and market leader, with over half of the market. You have been given the following information about Utoxx and Meetox for the year just ended.

Statement of profit or loss	Utoxx	Meetox
	£000	*£000*
Turnover	12,000	50,000
Cost of production		
Direct (raw) materials	2,800	8,600
Direct labour	1,900	4,200
Fixed production overheads	1,500	9,000
Total cost of sales	6,200	21,800
Gross profit	**5,800**	**28,200**
Selling and distribution costs	1,200	2,000
Administration costs	950	2,500
Advertising costs	900	18,000
Net profit	2,750	5,700

Other information		Utoxx	Meetox
Number of units sold	**Units**	1,200,000	4,500,000
Net assets	*(£000)*	10,000	18,000

Calculate the performance indicators to complete the following table for Utoxx and Meetox:

Give answers to two decimal places.

	Utoxx	Meetox
Selling price per unit		
Material cost per unit		
Labour cost per unit		
Fixed production overheads per unit		
Gross profit margin		
Net profit margin		
Advertising cost as % of turnover		
Return on net assets		

7   Measuring performance – further aspects

7.1   Control Limited makes a single product and uses standard costing.

Each unit has a standard labour time of 20 minutes. During November the budget was to produce 45,000 units.

In November 44,100 units were manufactured, and this took 15,200 labour hours.

Complete the following table by inserting the control ratios calculated as percentages to two decimal places.

Efficiency Ratio	
Activity Ratio (or Production Volume Ratio)	
Capacity Ratio	

7.2   Your organisation needs to send a parcel to an address on the other side of the city. It should arrive as soon as possible, but by tomorrow at the latest. Three alternatives have been suggested:

- Hire a taxi straight away to take the parcel. It will take about an hour and will cost £40.

- Send the parcel with a national 'overnight' parcel delivery service. This guarantees delivery by 9am tomorrow. The cost is £15.

- Give the parcel to John, who works in your office. He intends to visit his grandmother tomorrow or the next day, and she lives close to where the parcel needs to be delivered. Since he is going anyway, he won't charge to deliver the parcel.

By ticking the appropriate columns in the table, decide which alternative is the most economic, most efficient and most effective, from your organisation's point of view.

✔

	Economic	Efficient	Effective
Use a taxi			
Use national 'overnight' service			
Let John take it			

7.3 Complete the following table by selecting a valid method of calculation for each performance indicator

Performance Indicator	Calculation
(a) Labour efficiency (or efficiency ratio)	**1** $\dfrac{\text{(Sales – Cost of Materials and Bought-in Services)}}{\text{Number of Employees}}$
(b) Labour capacity (or capacity ratio)	**2** $\dfrac{\text{Standard Hours for Actual Production}}{\text{Budgeted Standard Hours}}$ x 100
(c) Added value per employee	**3** $\dfrac{\text{Unfulfilled Orders (in units)}}{\text{Annual Sales (in units)}}$ x 12
(d) Average delay in completing an order in months	**4** Sales – Cost of Materials and Bought-in Services
(e) Activity (or production volume) ratio	**5** $\dfrac{\text{Sales}}{\text{Labour Hours Worked}}$
(f) Value added	**6** $\dfrac{\text{Sales}}{\text{Units Sold}}$
(g) Average sales price per hour of labour	**7** $\dfrac{\text{Actual Hours Worked}}{\text{Budgeted Standard Hours}}$ x 100
(h) Average sales price per unit	**8** $\dfrac{\text{Standard Hours for Actual Production}}{\text{Actual Hours Worked}}$ x 100

7.4   The four perspectives used by the balanced scorecard are:

- Financial
- Customer
- Internal
- Innovation and Learning

The following table shows what each perspective is concerned with and ratios that can be used to measure aspects of that perspective.

Complete the table by inserting the correct perspective in each row.

Perspective	What it is concerned with	Typical ratios that can be used
	Technical excellence and quality issues	Added Value, Cost of Quality, Reject Rates, Sales returns (due to quality issues) as a % of net sales.
	Customer satisfaction and loyalty	Delivery times (or order backlogs), Repeat orders from customers, Sales returns as a % of net sales.
	Improvement of existing products or services, and development of new products or services	R & D Expenditure (or as %), Revenue from new products (or as %).
	Satisfying the shareholders, primarily by generating profits	Gross Profit %, Operating Profit %, ROCE, Added Value.

8 Scenario planning

8.1 Tinnitt Limited, a canned food manufacturer, currently makes two products in its factory. The first is baked beans, and the second is garden peas. Both are sold in tins.

The following budgeted operating statement relates to the next year, and assumes that both products will be manufactured in-house. It is based on making and selling 2,000,000 units of baked beans, and 1,000,000 units of garden peas.

	£000 Beans	£000 Peas	£000 Total
Sales	400	220	620
Variable costs of production	120	80	200
Direct fixed costs of production	80	70	150
Shared fixed costs of production	100	50	150
Gross profit	100	20	120
Administration costs			40
Selling and distribution costs			30
Operating profit			50

Consideration is being given to an option to buy in ready made tinned peas at £0.14 per unit. This would save both the variable costs of production and the direct fixed costs of production of that product. Shared fixed costs of production would remain the same in total. The number of units of tinned peas sold would be unchanged.

If the decision were made to buy in the tinned peas, then the released manufacturing space could be used to increase the manufacture and sales of baked beans to 2,500,000 units, with some spare capacity remaining. The direct fixed costs of baked bean production would be unchanged by this. To cope with the increased total volume of sales, the selling and distribution costs would increase by £5,000, but administration costs would remain unchanged.

Complete the table on the following page to show a budgeted operating statement based on the position if the decision were made to buy in tinned peas and increase production of baked beans.

	Baked Beans	Garden Peas	Total
Volume (units)	2,500,000	1,000,000	
	£000	£000	£000
Sales			
Variable costs of production / purchase			
Direct fixed costs of production			
Previously shared fixed costs of production			
Gross profit			
Administration costs			
Selling and distribution costs			
Operating profit			

8.2   Beta Limited manufactures toothpaste and is considering launching an improved version to replace the current product. It will be sold in smaller packs since it will be most effective when less quantity is used.

- Current sales volume is 2.0 million units per annum and this is not expected to change.

- Current fixed production costs are £0.6 million.

- Current labour cost per unit is £1.05 which is completely variable.

- Current material cost per unit is £1.45 and is completely variable.

- Assume stock levels are kept at zero.

- Variable material cost of the new product will be £0.30 less per unit than the current toothpaste.

- Selling price will be increased from £5.50 to £6.00.

- Fixed selling and distribution costs will reduce from £600,000 to £500,000.

- Additional investment in assets will be £8 million which will be depreciated at £800,000 per annum.

- All other costs will remain the same.

(a) Calculate the total annual increase in profit by completing the table below.

	Units	**Price/cost**	**Total £**
Additional revenue			
Savings on materials			
Reduction in selling and distribution costs			
Additional depreciation			
Additional annual profit			

(b) Based on the new product, calculate the performance measures shown in the following table to help understand any additional risk.

Return on additional investment (%)	
Total fixed costs	
Contribution per unit	
Break even sales volume in units	
Margin of safety (%)	

8.3 The table below shows the current situation for a company that buys and sells a single product. Current sales are 2,500 units per month, based on a selling price of £15.

Inventory is valued at variable cost and is equal to 3 months' sales. Customers take 2.5 months to pay. Payables relate to variable costs and are paid in 2 months.

A suggestion has been made to reduce the selling price by 20% to £12, which it is thought will result in an increased sales volume of 40%.

Complete the table based on the proposal, assuming that net current asset periods remain the same.

	Current Position	Proposed Position
Monthly Statement of Profit or Loss	£	£
Sales	37,500	
Variable Costs	25,000	
Fixed Costs	5,000	
Operating Profit	7,500	
Net Current Assets		
Inventory	75,000	
Receivables	93,750	
Less Payables	(50,000)	
Total Net Current Assets (exc cash)	118,750	

8.4 Chippum Limited makes frozen potato chips from raw potatoes. The potatoes are first machine washed, and then put through a peeling and slicing machine where the chips are cut to shape. At this stage a quality check is carried out by staff who manually pick out from the conveyor system and discard any chips that have blemishes. The chips are then cooked, frozen and bagged ready for sale.

The manager has been investigating the purchase of automated quality control line equipment that would eliminate the need for the majority of employees. The purchase and installation of the equipment would cost £600,000, and would be depreciated at £120,000 per year.

The following statement of profit or loss is based on the next year's operation, assuming the current working practices, and production of 1 million packs of chips.

	£000
Sales	1,200
less:	
Variable material cost	300
Variable labour cost	250
Contribution	650
less:	
Fixed production costs	100
Fixed administration costs	300
Operating profit	250

The net operating assets of the business are currently £1,600,000.

If the automated quality control line is installed:

- labour costs will reduce to £90,000 per year, regardless of the production level

- fixed production costs will increase by £20,000 per year, in addition to the depreciation expense

- other costs will be unchanged

The company's cost of capital is 5%, and discount factors over the five year life of the project are as follows:

Year	Discount factor 5%	Year	Discount factor 5%
0	1.00	3	0.864
1	0.952	4	0.823
2	0.907	5	0.784

The automated line will be paid for immediately and have no value at the end of the five year project. Assume that sales and costs remain at the same level for each of the five years, and occur at the end of each year.

Using the following table, calculate the net present value of the mechanisation project.

Year	Cash Outflow £	Cash Savings £	Discount Factor	Present Value £
0				
1				
2				
3				
4				
5				
Net Present Value				

Chapter activities answers

1 Management accounting techniques

1.1 The trend in prices is an increase of **£0.30** per month.

1.2 (c) 120 *(Cost per kilo £18.00 compared with £15.00)*

1.3 (a) The cost index in April was 135 and the increase from January to April is 8.0%

1.4

Feature	Marginal Costing	Absorption Costing
Can be used to set a minimum selling price	✔	
Complies with standard IAS 2 for inventory valuation		✔
Can be used for planning and control but is of limited use for decision making		✔
Can be used in conjunction with break even analysis	✔	
Can be used in conjunction with 'full cost plus' pricing		✔
Is often used in conjunction with discounted cash flow decision making techniques	✔	

1.5 (a)

Year	Detail	Cash Flow £	Discount Factor	Present Value £
0	Purchase and Installation	(8,000)	1.000	(8,000)
1	Savings and increased house sale proceeds	200	0.909	182
2		200	0.826	165
3		200	0.751	150
4		200	0.683	137
5		5,200	0.621	3,229
Net Present Value				(4,137)

(b) The net present value of the scheme is **negative** so from a financial point of view the scheme is **not worthwhile**.

1.6 The difference in total cost of £152,000 – £100,000 = £52,000 is due to the variable costs for 18,000 – 10,000 = 8,000 units.

Variable costs per unit are therefore

£52,000 / 8,000   = £6.50 per unit.

Fixed costs account for the difference between the variable costs and the total costs.

At 10,000 units:

Total costs	£100,000
Variable costs (10,000 x £6.50)	£65,000
Therefore fixed costs are	£35,000

The same answer could be obtained using the 18,000 unit costs.

1.7 The difference in total cost of £606,000 – £500,000 = £106,000 is due to

- the step in fixed costs of £40,000

- the variable costs for 28,000 – 22,000 = 6,000 units.

Variable costs per unit are therefore

(£106,000 – £40,000) / 6,000   = £11.00 per unit.

Fixed costs account for the difference between the variable costs and the total costs.

At 22,000 units:

Total costs	£500,000
Variable costs (22,000 x £11)	£242,000
Therefore stepped fixed costs are	£258,000

At 28,000 units:

Total costs	£606,000
Variable costs (28,000 x £11)	£308,000
Therefore stepped fixed costs are	£298,000

This also agrees with the step in the fixed cost of £40,000.

2 Standard costing – direct costs

2.1 (d) £600 Favourable

2.2 (b) £1,300 Adverse

2.3 (a) £87,500

2.4

Variance	£	A/F
Direct material (paint) price variance	130	F
Direct material (sheet steel) usage variance	750	A
Direct labour rate variance	2,050	A
Direct labour efficiency variance	6,000	F

Variance Workings:

Paint price:	(650 litres x £5) – £3,120	= £130 F
Steel usage:	((11,500 x 3) – 35,000) x £1.50	= £750 A
Labour rate:	(4,100 x £12) – £51,250)	= £2,050 A
Labour efficiency:	((11,500 x 0.4) – 4,100) x £12	= £6,000 F

2.5 **(a)** The standard material cost per kg is **£1.40**

(b) The standard quantity of material to make one unit is **0.5 kg**

(c) The standard cost of the materials to make one unit is **£0.70**

Workings:

(a) (£15,400 + £700) / 11,500 kg = £1.40 per kg

(b) (£700 / £1.40 = 500 kg) + 11,500 kg = 12,000 kg

12,000 kg / 24,000 units = 0.5 kg per unit

(c) £1.40 x 0.5 kg per unit = £0.70

2.6 The standard time to make 2,000 units is **400** hours.
Working: 2,000 units x 12/60 hours

The standard labour rate is **£10** per hour.
Working: £450 = (445 – 400) hours x Standard rate
Therefore Standard rate = £450 / 45 hours

2.7   The standard hourly rate is **£11.00** per hour.

Working: Standard cost of 5,500 hours is £59,400 + £1,100 = £60,500

Standard hourly rate is £60,500 / 5,500 hours

2.8

Budgeted / Standard cost of materials for actual production			£97,500
Variances:	**Favourable £**	**Adverse £**	
Direct material price	1,560		
Direct material usage		3,900	
Total variance		2,340	+£2,340
Actual cost of materials for actual production			£99,840

2.9

Budgeted / Standard cost of labour for actual production			£3,750.00
Variances:	**Favourable £**	**Adverse £**	
Direct labour rate		107.50	
Direct labour efficiency		87.50	
Total variance		195.00	+£195.00
Actual cost of labour for actual production			£3,945.00

3 Standard costing – variable and fixed overheads

3.1

1 unit of Zed	Quantity	Cost per unit £	Total cost £
Material	12 kg	8.50	102.00
Labour	0.6 hour	15.00	9.00
Fixed costs	1 unit	80.00	80.00
Total			191.00

3.2 The fixed overhead volume variance is **£100,000 adverse**.

The fixed overhead expenditure variance is **£20,000 favourable.**

3.3 The fixed overhead efficiency variance is **£4,800 adverse**.

The fixed overhead capacity variance is **£11,200 adverse.**

3.4

	Variance £	A / F	Variance £	A / F
Expenditure Variance			2,000	F
Capacity Variance	1,500	A		
Efficiency Variance	4,500	A		
Volume Variance			6,000	A
Total Fixed Overhead Variances			4,000	A

3.5 (a) and (c) are false; the others are true.

3.6

Budgeted / Standard fixed cost for actual production			£437,500
Variances:	**Favourable £**	**Adverse £**	
Fixed overhead expenditure	10,500		
Fixed overhead volume	7,500		
Total variance	18,000		–£18,000
Actual fixed cost for actual production			£419,500

3.7 **(a)** Variable overhead expenditure variance:

(5,400 direct labour hours x £3.50) – £19,100

= £200 Adverse

(b) Variable overhead efficiency variance:

(0.5 hours x 10,500 units x £3.50) – (5,400 hours x £3.50)

= £18,375 – £18,900

= £525 Adverse

3.8 **(a)** Variable overhead expenditure variance:

(1,990 machine hours £13*) – £27,600

= £1,730 Adverse

* Standard hourly rate = £1.30 x 10

(b) Variable overhead efficiency variance:

(0.1 hours x 20,250 units x £13) – (1,990 hours x £13)

= £26,325 – £25,870

= £455 Favourable

4   Standard costing – further analysis

4.1

Budgeted cost for actual production			£39,165
Variances:	Favourable £	Adverse £	
Direct materials (liquid cleaner) price	975		
Direct materials (liquid cleaner) usage		125	
Direct materials (bottles) price	96		
Direct materials (bottles) usage		60	
Direct labour rate	170		
Direct labour efficiency		330	
Fixed overhead expenditure		500	
Fixed overhead volume	350		
Total variances	1,591	1,015	–£576
Actual cost of actual production			£38,589

4.2

Budgeted cost for actual production			£81,120
Variances:	Favourable £	Adverse £	
Direct materials price	80		
Direct materials usage		80	
Direct labour rate		600	
Direct labour efficiency		400	
Fixed overhead expenditure		2,300	
Fixed overhead capacity	4,500		
Fixed overhead efficiency		2,000	
Total variances	4,580	5,380	+£800
Actual cost of actual production			£81,920

4.2   (continued)

Variance workings:

DMPV	(800 x £4) – £3,120	= £80 F
DMUV	[(3 litres x 260) – 800 litres] x £4	= £80 A
DLRV	(1,340 hrs x £10) – £14,000	= £600 A
DLEV	[(5 hrs x 260) – 1,340 hrs] x £10	= £400 A
FO Exp	£62,500 – £64,800	= £2,300 A
FO Cap	(1,340 x £50) – (1,250 x £50)	= £4,500 F
FO Eff	(1,300 x £50) – (1,340 x £50)	= £2,000 A

4.3

Direct Material Usage Variance			Part of variance caused by change in product specification			Part of variance caused by unknown factors		
	£	A / F		£	A / F		£	A / F
	2,400	F		9,000	F		6,600	A

4.4

Email

To: Production Director

From: Accounting Technician

Date: xx

Subject: Reasons for Variances

The following sets out some possible reasons for the adverse variances that occurred based on the September operations.

The direct material price variance relates to the buying price of raw potatoes. The recent UK weather created a poor potato harvest, and the subsequent shortage of potatoes led to a price increase. This price increase would have been across the whole UK market.

The direct material usage variance relates to the additional cost incurred due to using more raw potatoes than expected to make the average bag of frozen chips. This appears to be due to the poor quality of potatoes, which meant that more partly processed output had to be rejected.

The adverse direct labour rate variance may be caused by the use of overtime rates to pay for the additional time required by the quality control operatives. The overtime rate was paid to satisfy the need to spend more time discarding the blemished chips that occurred due to the quality of the potatoes.

The direct labour efficiency variance is also related to the work of the labour-intensive quality control function. Since there were so many blemished chips to be removed, the conveyor had to be slowed down, and this increased the labour time needed to check the output.

The fixed overhead expenditure variance relates to the additional fixed overheads incurred in September. One such cost was incurred when the conveyor broke down and a contractor was utilised to supply and fit replacement parts.

The fixed overhead volume variance is caused by spreading the fixed overheads over a smaller amount of output than was budgeted. It seems likely that in September the output was lower than budgeted due to the greater proportion of the input that was rejected in the form of blemished chips, together with the linked issue of the slow running of the conveyor.

Overall the adverse variances mean that the actual cost of the September production was £30,000 more than the standard cost of the same production level.

4.5

Budgeted / Standard variable cost for actual production			£903,825
Budgeted fixed costs			£200,000
Variances	**Favourable £**	**Adverse £**	
Direct materials (drink) price		29,300	
Direct materials (drink) usage		1,050	
Direct materials (cans) price		0	
Direct materials (cans) usage		200	
Direct labour rate	300		
Direct labour efficiency	300		
Variable overhead expenditure		400	
Variable overhead efficiency	175		
Fixed overhead expenditure		3,500	
Total variance		33,675	+£33,675
Actual cost of actual production			£1,137,500

Workings:

Budgeted variable cost for actual production:

(£630,000 + £240,000 + £36,000 + £21,000) x 5,850,000 / 6,000,000 = £903,825

Direct materials (drink) price variance:

(2,930,000 litres x £0.21*) − £644,600 = £29,300 A

*£630,000 / 3,000,000 litres

Direct materials (drink) usage variance:

((5,850,000 units x 0.5*) − 2,930,000) x £0.21 = £1,050 A

*500 ml = 0.5 litre

Direct materials (cans) price variance:

(5,855,000 units x £0.04) − £234,200 = £0

Direct materials (cans) usage variance:

$(5,850,000 - 5,855,000) \times £0.04 = £200$ A

Direct labour rate variance:

$(2,900 \times £12^*) - £34,500 = £300$ F

*£36,000 / 3,000 hours

Direct labour efficiency variance:

$((5,850,000 \text{ units} \times 0.0005 \text{ hours per unit}^*) - 2,900 \text{ hours}) \times £12 = £300$ F

*3,000 hours / 6,000,000 units

Variable overhead expenditure variance:

$(2,900 \times £7^*) - £20,700 = £400$ A

*£21,000 / 3,000 hours

Variable overhead efficiency variance:

$((5,850,000 \text{ units} \times 0.0005 \text{ hours per unit}) - 2,900 \text{ hours}) \times £7 = £175$ F

Fixed overhead expenditure variance:

$£200,000 - £203,500 = £3,500$ A

Measuring quality

5.1

Maximum production cost per unit	£5.25
Build up of maximum production cost per unit:	
Materials	£1.85 (balancing figure)
Labour	£1.40
Overheads	£2.00
Maximum cost per kilo for material T	£3.70

5.2 **(a)**

Year	0	1	2	3	4
Cash flow *(£)*	15,000	800	800	800	(3,200)
Discount factor	1.00	0.952	0.907	0.864	0.823
Present value *(£)*	15,000	762	726	691	(2,634)
Net present cost *(£)*	14,545				

(b)

Year	0	1	2	3	4
Lease costs *(£)*	4,100	4,100	4,100	4,100	0
Discount factor	1.00	0.952	0.907	0.864	0.823
Present value *(£)*	4,100	3,903	3,719	3,542	0
Net present cost *(£)*	15,264				

(c) Based on the calculations it is best to **purchase** each van, which saves a net present amount of **£719**.

5.3 **(a)**

	£
Sales price per unit	40.00
Profit margin	18.00
Total costs	22.00
Fixed cost per unit	12.00
Labour cost per unit	6.00
Maximum material cost per unit	4.00
Target cost per kilogram	20.00

(b) The trade price quoted on the supplier's price list is £25 per kilogram. The purchasing manager has negotiated a discount of 15%. The discount should be **rejected** because the £25 reduces to **£21.25** which is **above** the Target cost.

(c) The minimum percentage discount needed to achieve the Target cost is **20%**

5.4

	Prevention Costs	Appraisal Costs	Internal Failure Costs	External Failure Costs
Production staff training costs	✔			
Costs of customer complaints section				✔
Costs of re-inspection of reworked products			✔	
Inspection of work in progress		✔		
Testing of finished goods		✔		
Loss of customer goodwill				✔
Customer compensation payments				✔

6 Measuring performance

6.1 (a) 7

(b) 10

(c) 9

(d) 8

(e) 2

(f) 1

(g) 5

(h) 3

(i) 4

(j) 6

6.2

	20-8	20-7
Gross Profit %	24.88	22.96
Return on Capital Employed %	18.35	17.99
Operating Profit as % Sales	13.88	12.76
Current Ratio	1.61	1.00
Asset Turnover	1.32	1.41
Quick Ratio	1.13	0.63
Trade Receivables Days	70	67
Trade Payables Days	108	110
Gearing Ratio %	41.14	53.46

6.3

Performance Indicator	20-8	20-7	Comments
Gross Profit %	24.88	22.96	The profit as a percentage of sales (after taking into account just the cost of sales) has improved from the first year to the second
Return on Capital Employed %	18.35	17.99	The operating profit as a percentage of total resources has increased from year to year
Operating Profit as % Sales	13.88	12.76	The profit before interest as a percentage of turnover has increased in the later year
Current Ratio	1.61	1.00	There are more current assets compared to current liabilities in the later year
Asset Turnover	1.32	1.41	There is less value of sales compared to total resources in the later year
Quick Ratio	1.13	0.63	After excluding inventory, there are more current assets compared to current liabilities in the later year
Trade Receivables Days	70	67	Credit customers are taking slightly longer on average to pay in the later year than they were in the previous year
Trade Payables Days	108	158	The company is paying its credit suppliers considerably more quickly in the later year
Gearing Ratio %	41.14	46.76	A smaller proportion of the capital employed is based on fixed interest capital in the later year

6.4

	Utoxx	Meetox
Selling price per unit	£10.00	£11.11
Material cost per unit	£2.33	£1.91
Labour cost per unit	£1.58	£0.93
Fixed production overheads per unit	£1.25	£2.00
Gross profit margin	48.33%	56.40%
Net profit margin	22.92%	11.40%
Advertising cost as % of turnover	7.50%	36.00%
Return on net assets	27.50%	31.67%

7 | Measuring performance – further aspects

7.1

Efficiency Ratio	96.71%
Activity Ratio (or Production Volume Ratio)	98.00%
Capacity Ratio	101.33%

7.2

	Economic	Efficient	Effective
Use a taxi			✔
Use national 'overnight' service		✔	
Let John take it	✔		

7.3
   (a)   8

   (b)   7

   (c)   1

   (d)   3

   (e)   2

   (f)   4

   (g)   5

   (h)   6

7.4

Perspective	What it is concerned with	Typical ratios that can be used
Internal	Technical excellence and quality issues	Added Value, Cost of Quality, Reject Rates, Sales returns (due to quality issues) as a % of net sales.
Customer	Customer satisfaction and loyalty	Delivery times (or order backlogs), Repeat orders from customers, Sales returns as a % of net sales.
Innovation and Learning	Improvement of existing products or services, and development of new products or services	R & D Expenditure (or as %), Revenue from new products (or as %).
Financial	Satisfying the shareholders, primarily by generating profits	Gross Profit %, Operating Profit %, ROCE, Added Value.

8 Scenario planning

8.1

	Baked Beans	Garden Peas	Total
Volume (units)	2,500,000	1,000,000	
	£000	£000	£000
Sales	500	220	720
Variable costs of production / purchase	150	140	290
Direct fixed costs of production	80	0	80
Previously shared fixed costs of production	150	0	150
Gross profit	120	80	200
Administration costs			40
Selling and distribution costs			35
Operating profit			125

8.2 (a)

	Units	Price/cost £	Total £
Additional revenue	2,000,000	0.50	1,000,000
Savings on materials	2,000,000	0.30	600,000
Reduction in selling and distribution costs			100,000
Additional depreciation			(800,000)
Additional annual profit			900,000

(b)

Return on additional investment (%)	11.25%
Total fixed costs	£1,900,000
Contribution per unit	£3.80
Break even sales volume in units	500,000
Margin of safety (%)	75%

8.3

	Current Position	Proposed Position
Monthly Statement of Profit or Loss	£	£
Sales	37,500	42,000
Variable Costs	25,000	35,000
Fixed Costs	5,000	5,000
Operating Profit	7,500	2,000
Net Current Assets		
Inventory	75,000	105,000
Receivables	93,750	105,000
Less Payables	(50,000)	(70,000)
Total Net Current Assets (exc cash)	118,750	140,000

8.4

Year	Cash Outflow	Cash Savings	Discount Factor	Present Value
	£	£		£
0	600,000		1.000	(600,000)
1		140,000	0.952	133,280
2		140,000	0.907	126,980
3		140,000	0.864	120,960
4		140,000	0.823	115,220
5		140,000	0.784	109,760
	Net Present Value			6,200

Cash savings:

Labour savings	£160,000
Less increased production costs	£ 20,000
	£140,000

Practice
assessment 1

Task 1

(a) The following information has been calculated for the production of 1 unit of Exe:

- Each unit will require 1.3 kilograms of material at a cost of £4.50 per kilogram
- Each unit will require 0.2 hours of labour at a total cost of £3.60
- Fixed overheads total £50,000 and the estimated output will be 25,000 units of Exe
- Fixed overheads are absorbed on a labour hour basis

Complete the standard cost card below.

1 unit of Exe	Quantity	Cost per unit £	Total cost £
Material			
Labour			
Fixed costs			
Total			

(b) A manufacturer uses 30,000 kg of material to make 150,000 units. The standard quantity of material for each unit is:

| kg |

Task 2

(a)   A company purchases 18,000 kilograms of material at a cost of £91,080. The standard cost per kilogram is £5.10. The total material price variance is:

✔

(a) £720 Favourable	
(b) £0.04 Favourable	
(c) £720 Adverse	
(d) £0.04 Adverse	

(b)   A company used 11,000 kilograms of material at a cost of £47,300. The production was 1,200 units, for which the standard usage is 10,800 kilograms of material at a total standard cost of £43,200. The material usage variance is:

✔

(a) 200 kg Adverse	
(b) £3,300 Adverse	
(c) £800 Adverse	
(d) £860 Adverse	

(c)   A company expects to produce 10,000 units of Y using 5,000 labour hours. The standard cost of labour is £20 per hour. If the actual output is 12,500 units, what is the standard labour cost for this output?

✔

(a) £500,000	
(b) £250,000	
(c) £125,000	
(d) £50,000	

(d)   A company used 11,000 kilograms of material at a cost of £47,300. The production was 1,200 units, for which the standard usage is 10,800 kilograms of material at a total standard cost of £43,200. The material price variance is:

✔

(a) £800 Adverse	
(b) £3,300 Adverse	
(c) £3,240 Adverse	
(d) £860 Adverse	

Task 3

(a) You have been given the following information:

- Budgeted overheads are £400,000

- Budgeted output is 40,000 units

- Actual output is 42,000 units

- Actual overheads are £415,000

The fixed overhead volume variance is £ [   ] **adverse / favourable.**

The fixed overhead expenditure variance is £ [   ] **adverse / favourable.**

(b) You have been given the following information:

- Budgeted overheads are £90,000

- Budgeted output is 15,000 units and 5,000 labour hours

- Actual output is 14,400 units and 4,950 actual labour hours

- Actual overheads are £93,000

The fixed overhead efficiency variance is £ [   ] **adverse / favourable.**

The fixed overhead capacity variance is £ [   ] **adverse / favourable.**

Task 4

A company packs instant coffee into jars.

The following budgetary control report has been provided:

	Budget		Actual	
Production (jars)		50,000		51,500
Instant coffee	20,000 kg	£60,000	20,650 kg	£62,260
Glass jars	50,000 units	£2,000	51,700 units	£2,050
Direct labour	200 hours	£3,600	220 hours	£3,850
Fixed overheads		£10,000		£10,150
Total cost		£75,600		£78,310

The following variances have been accurately calculated, although for some it is not known whether they are adverse or favourable:

Fixed overhead expenditure	£150 A
Direct materials (instant coffee) price	£310
Direct materials (glass jars) price	£18 F
Direct materials (instant coffee) usage	£150 A
Direct materials (glass jars) usage	£8
Direct labour rate	£110 F
Direct labour efficiency	£252
Fixed overhead volume	£300

Complete the following operating statement, including the budgeted cost for the 51,500 units of production and the variances. Make sure that the total agrees with the actual cost of production.

Budgeted cost for actual production			£
Variances:	**Favourable £**	**Adverse £**	
Direct materials (instant coffee) price			
Direct materials (instant coffee) usage			
Direct materials (glass jars) price			
Direct materials (glass jars) usage			
Direct labour rate			
Direct labour efficiency			
Fixed overhead expenditure			
Fixed overhead volume			
Total variances			£
Actual cost of actual production			£

Task 5

(a) The table below contains the last three months' cost per kilogram for product Beta.

January	February	March
Actual price was £35.60	Actual price was £30.10	Actual price was £29.00
Seasonal variation was +£5.20	Seasonal variation was –£0.90	Seasonal variation was –£2.60

The trend in prices is an **increase/decrease** of £ [   ] per month.

(b) A company has provided the following information:

	January	February	March
Total cost	£120,000	£143,925	£143,100
Total quantity purchased	8,000 kg	9,500 kg	9,000 kg

The cost index for March based upon January being the base period of 100 is:

		✔
(a)	119	
(b)	113	
(c)	143	
(d)	106	

(c) The cost per unit of a product has decreased from £250 in January to £244 in April. The cost per unit was £200 when the index was rebased to 100.

		✔
(a)	The cost index in April was 125 and the decrease from January to April is 6.0%	
(b)	The cost index in April was 122 and the decrease from January to April is 2.4%	
(c)	The cost index in April is 122 and the decrease from January to April is 2.5%	
(d)	The cost index in April is 244 and the decrease from January to April is 2.4%	

Task 6

Frooyo manufactures fruit yoghurts, using mechanised production lines. The production line for strawberry yoghurt is set to mix 400 grams of yoghurt with 100 grams of strawberries into each 500 gram pot. This minimum quantity of strawberries in each pot is displayed on the pot for consumers to see.

The monthly report on the strawberry yoghurt production line in September noted the following variances.

Material Variances	Favourable £	Adverse £
Direct material (yoghurt) price		500
Direct material (yoghurt) usage	20,000	
Direct material (strawberries) price		30,000
Direct material (strawberries) usage		50,000

During September, 2 million pots of strawberry yoghurt were produced. The standard price of yoghurt is 20p per kg, and the standard price of strawberries is 50p per kg.

You have discovered the following information about the September production of strawberry yoghurt.

- The strawberries are sourced in the UK. Due to poor UK weather the price rose by 10p per kilo above standard.

- Each yoghurt pot is automatically weighed to check that it contains a full 500 grams.

- The production equipment malfunctioned and inserted more strawberries and less yoghurt into each pot than it was supposed to. The total weight of each pot remained accurate.

- The equipment malfunction was not detected until after the month end.

- Variances of more than £1,000 are considered significant.

Using the above information, prepare a report for the Production Director. The report should:

- Explain and provide reasons for each significant material variance, and

- Suggest strategies that may minimise similar variances in future.

Report

To: Production Director

From: Accounting Technician

Date: xx

Subject: Report on September production of strawberry yoghurt

Price Variances

•   Explanation and reasons

•   Future strategies

Usage Variances

•   Explanation and reasons

•   Future strategies

Task 7

Cosy Hotels Limited operates a number of small hotels. One of its competitors is Lush Hotels. You have been given the following information about Cosy Hotels and Lush Hotels for the year just ended.

Statement of Profit or Loss	Cosy	Lush
	£	£
Turnover	1,312,500	1,680,000
Variable costs		
Food	350,000	432,000
Laundry	87,500	120,000
Cleaning	262,500	288,000
Total variable costs	700,000	840,000
Contribution	**612,500**	**840,000**
Selling and marketing costs	300,000	350,000
Administration costs	155,000	163,000
Financial costs	85,000	118,000
Net profit	**72,500**	**209,000**
Other information	**Cosy**	**Lush**
Number of room-nights occupied	17,500	24,000
Number of room-nights available	35,000	30,000

Calculate the performance indicators to complete the following table for Cosy Hotels and Lush Hotels:

Give answers to two decimal places.

	Cosy	Lush
Selling price per room-night		
Occupancy rate (%)		
Variable costs per room-night		
Contribution per room-night		
Contribution / sales ratio (%)		
Net profit margin		
Selling and marketing cost as % of turnover		

Task 8

Gamma Limited manufactures a food paste that is currently sold in jars and is considering launching a more concentrated version to replace the current product. It will be sold in small tubes.

- Current sales volume is 3.0 million units per annum and this is not expected to change.

- Current fixed production costs are £0.7 million.

- Current labour cost per unit is £0.55 which is completely variable.

- Current material cost per unit is £0.95 and is completely variable.

- Assume stock levels are kept at zero.

- Variable material cost of the new product will be £0.15 less per unit than the current food product.

- Selling price will be increased from £2.60 to £2.70.

- Fixed selling and distribution costs will reduce from £400,000 to £250,000.

- Additional investment in assets will be £4 million which will be depreciated at £400,000 per annum.

- All other costs will remain the same.

(a)   Calculate the total annual increase in profit by completing the table below.

	Units	Price/cost £	Total £
Additional revenue			
Savings on materials			
Reduction in selling and distribution costs			
Additional depreciation			
Additional annual profit			

(b) Based on the new product, calculate the performance measures shown in the following table to help understand any additional risk.

Return on additional investment (%)	
Total fixed costs	
Contribution per unit	
Break even sales volume in units	
Margin of safety (%)	

Task 9

Omega Limited is considering designing a new product, and will use target costing to arrive at the target cost of the product. You have been given the following information and asked to calculate the target cost for labour so that the production manager can calculate the labour time that should be allowed for manufacture.

- The price at which the product will be sold is £30

- The company has firm orders for 20,000 units at this price for the first year

- The fixed costs are £180,000 per year

- The labour rate is currently £15 per hour

- The required profit margin is 40%

- The material requirement is 250 grams per unit

- The material cost is £16 per kg

(a) Calculate the target time for the labour component of the product, using the following table.

	£
Sales price per unit	
Profit margin	
Total costs	
Fixed cost per unit	
Material cost per unit	
Maximum labour cost per unit	
Target labour time per unit (minutes)	

(b) Complete the following statement:

The Trade Union negotiator wished to increase the hourly labour rate by 6%. He believes that in return, employees can produce each unit in 18 minutes if they are provided with additional training. If achievable, this proposal should be **accepted / rejected** because it **reduces / increases** the labour cost per unit. The labour cost under this proposal would be

£ [   ]   per unit.

Task 10

Wye Limited is developing a new product and a colleague has prepared forecast information based upon two scenarios. The forecast statement of profit or loss for both scenarios is shown below.

- Scenario 1 is to set the price at £15 per unit with sales of 80,000 units each year.
- Scenario 2 is to set the price at £13 per unit with sales of 120,000 units each year.

Forecast Statement of Profit or Loss	Scenario 1	Scenario 2
	£	£
Turnover	1,200,000	1,560,000
Cost of production		
Direct (raw) materials	240,000	360,000
Direct labour	160,000	252,000
Fixed production overheads	560,000	560,000
Total cost of sales	960,000	1,172,000
Gross profit	240,000	388,000
Selling and distribution costs	80,000	115,000
Administration costs	60,000	60,000
Operating profit	100,000	213,000
	Scenario 1	**Scenario 2**
Gross profit margin	20.00%	24.87%
Operating profit margin	8.33%	13.65%
Direct materials as a percentage of turnover	20.00%	23.08%
Direct materials cost per unit	£3.00	£3.00
Direct labour cost per unit	£2.00	£2.10
Fixed production cost per unit	£7.00	£4.67

Draft a report for the Finance Director covering the following:

(a) An explanation of why the gross profit margins are different, referring to the following:

- Sales price and Sales volume
- Materials cost
- Labour cost
- Fixed production costs

(b) An explanation of why the operating profit margins are different.

(c) A recommendation, with reasons, as to which course of action to take.

Report

To: Finance Director   Subject: Scenarios 1 & 2

From: Accounting technician   Date: xx

(a) **Why are the gross profit margins different?**

• Sales Price / Sales Volume

• Materials

• Labour

• Fixed production costs

(b) **Why are the operating profit margins different?**

(c) **Recommendation, with reasons, as to which course of action to take**

Practice
assessment 2

Task 1

The budgeted and actual results for the month of August 20X4 are as follows:

	Budget		Actual	
Production units		25,000		27,000
Direct materials	56,250 kg	£28,125	61,000 kg	£29,280
Direct labour	5,000 hours	£45,000	5,200 hours	£47,320
Fixed overheads (absorbed on a unit basis)		£75,000		£77,500
Total		£148,125		£154,100

Complete the following table.

(a)	Standard quantity of labour per unit (in minutes)	
(b)	Budgeted quantity of materials to produce 27,000 units (in kilos)	
(c)	Budgeted quantity of labour to produce 27,000 units (in hours)	
(d)	Budgeted labour cost to produce 27,000 units (in £)	
(e)	Budgeted overhead absorption rate per unit (in £)	
(f)	Amount of over absorption of fixed overheads (in £)	

Task 2

(a) A company purchases 7,400 kilograms of material at a cost of £10,250. The material price variance is £260 adverse.

Complete the following sentence:

The standard cost per kilogram is   £ [   ] .

(b) A company purchases and uses 150,250 litres of material at a cost of £190,000. The budgeted production was 12,000 units which required 180,000 litres of material at a total standard cost of £225,000. The actual production was 9,950 units.

Complete the following sentence:

The material usage variance is   £ [   ]   **adverse / favourable.**

(c) A company expects to produce 24,000 units using 3,000 hours of labour. The standard cost of labour is £14 per hour. The actual output was 25,000 units. 3,100 hours were worked and 3,180 hours were paid at a total cost of £44,900.

Complete the following sentences:

The labour efficiency variance is   £ [   ]   **adverse / favourable** (excluding idle time).

The idle time variance is   £ [   ]   **adverse / favourable.**

Task 3

(a) Aye Limited operates a standard cost system in which production overheads are fixed and absorbed on a unit basis.

The budgeted production level is 35,000 units with budgeted fixed overhead costs of £157,500. The actual volume of production was 37,000 units, and the fixed overhead expenditure variance was £4,500 favourable.

Complete the following sentences:

The fixed overhead volume variance is £ [   ] **adverse / favourable**.

The actual fixed production overheads incurred were £ [   ] .

(b) Bee Limited operates a standard cost system in which production overheads are fixed and absorbed on a standard labour hour basis.

The data for the month is as follows:

	Budget	**Actual**
Production units	55,000	63,000
Direct labour hours	5,500	6,100
Direct labour costs	£66,000	£76,250
Fixed overhead costs	£107,250	£108,000

Complete the following table:

Variance	**Amount £**	**Adverse / Favourable**
Fixed overhead capacity		
Fixed overhead efficiency		

Task 4

The following budgetary control report has been provided, together with the variances calculated below.

	Budget		Actual	
Production (units)		19,000		21,500
Direct materials	7,600 kg	£22,040	8,820 kg	£24,682
Direct labour	380 hours	£6,080	450 hours	£7,425
Variable overheads	380 hours	£7,600	450 hours	£8,550
Fixed overheads		£190,000		£195,000
Total cost		£225,720		£235,657

The following variances have been calculated:

Variance	Amount £
Direct material price	896
Direct material usage	638
Direct labour rate	225
Direct labour efficiency	320
Variable overhead expenditure	450
Variable overhead efficiency	400
Fixed overhead expenditure	5,000

Complete the operating statement on the following page using marginal costing.

Budgeted variable cost for actual production			£
Budgeted fixed cost			£
Total budgeted cost for actual production			£
Variance:	**Favourable £**	**Adverse £**	
Direct material price			
Direct material usage			
Direct labour rate			
Direct labour efficiency			
Variable overhead expenditure			
Variable overhead efficiency			
Fixed overhead expenditure			
Total variance			£
Actual cost of actual production			£

Task 5

(a)   A foodstuff is used as a raw material by a processing company. The standard price of £540 per tonne was set when the material price index for this foodstuff was 189.5.

In August the company bought and used 230 tonnes of this foodstuff and the material price variance was calculated as £4,200 favourable. The price index for August was 187.6.

Calculate the information that is needed to complete the table below.

	Amount
Price per tonne based on August index (to nearest penny)	
Part of variance explained by change in index (to nearest £)	
Part of variance not explained by change in index (to nearest £)	
	%
Percentage reduction in index (to two decimal places)	

(b)   A raw material has had the following cost per kilo over the last few months:

	June	July	August
Cost per kilo	£531.26	£533.60	£535.94

Complete the following table with the expected cost per kilo later the same year:

	October	November
Cost per kilo		

(c)   The formula for linear regression for the cost of a certain raw material has been calculated as:

$y = 44.1x + 2,391.5$

'y' is the cost per tonne in £ and 'x' is the period.

August 20X4 was period 25.

Complete the following sentence:

The forecast cost per tonne in December 20X4 is £ [   ] to the nearest penny.

Task 6

You have been provided with the following information for the month just ended:

	Budget		Actual	
Production units		40,000		43,000
Direct labour	20,000 hours	£320,000	21,200 hours	£343,440

The finance director has asked you to write a note to help in the training of a junior accounting technician. The notes are to explain the calculation of the total direct labour variance and how this variance can be split into a rate variance and an efficiency variance.

Prepare a note explaining the total direct labour variance and how it can be split into a rate variance and an efficiency variance. Calculations should be used to illustrate the explanation.

Task 7

A company operates a marginal accounting system, and you have been provided with the following data based on two scenarios:

	Scenario 1	Scenario 2
Sales volume (units)	200,000	120,000
	£	£
Revenue	4,400,000	3,240,000
Contribution	1,200,000	1,320,000
Profit from operations	200,000	320,000
Net assets	1,600,000	1,400,000
Inventory (marginal cost)	420,000	350,000

(a) Complete the following performance indicators for scenarios 1 and 2. Give your answers to two decimal places.

	Scenario 1	Scenario 2
Return on net assets		
Inventory holding period in days		
Sales price per unit		
Marginal (variable) cost per unit		

(b) Complete the table below for scenario 3.

	Scenario 3
Net assets	£1,800,000
Contribution to sales ratio	50%
Fixed costs	£1,000,000
Return on net assets	10%
Profit (£)	
Contribution (£)	
Sales Revenue (£)	

continued

(c)   Select the correct ratio from the options below to calculate 'asset turnover'.

✔

(a)	Operating profit / Revenue	
(b)	Net assets / Revenue	
(c)	Revenue / Operating profit	
(d)	Revenue / Net assets	
(e)	Operating profit / Net assets	
(f)	Net assets / Operating profit	

Task 8

A company manufactures two products, Toll and Tall. The following information is available for the next month.

	Product Toll	Product Tall
	£ per unit	**£ per unit**
Selling price	700	500
Variable costs:		
Materials (£50 per kilogram)	300	100
Labour	160	170
Fixed costs:		
Production	125	125
Administration	50	50
Profit per unit	65	55
Monthly demand	5,000 units	4,500 units

The materials are in short supply and only 30,000 kilograms of materials will be available from the existing supplier.

(a)   Complete the table below.

	Product Toll	Product Tall
Contribution per unit		
Contribution per kilogram of material		
Priority ranking (1 or 2)		
Number of units to be made to maximise profit		
Total contribution for each product based on above numbers		

(b)   An alternative supplier can provide additional materials at a higher price. Complete the following sentence:

The price paid per kilogram for additional material must be less than £ [   ]

to be worthwhile.

Task 9

A company is considering manufacturing a new product, and will use target costing to develop its plans.

The selling price of the product will either be £25 (with an estimated demand of 200,000 units), or £20 (with an estimated demand of 300,000 units).

Stepped fixed production costs are £2,000,000 for up to 250,000 units and £2,400,000 for over this level.

Variable costs are yet to be determined, but are expected to be in the range of £8 to £12 per unit.

Company policy is for all new products to have a profit margin of 25%.

(a)   Complete the following table.

	Selling price £25	Selling price £20
Estimated demand (units)		
Target profit per unit		
Target total costs per unit		
Target fixed production costs per unit		
Target variable costs per unit		

(b)   Complete the following sentence:

A selling price of £ [   ] per unit would allow for target variable costs within the expected range.

Task 10

A company makes and sells a single product. The current and proposed positions are outlined below.

Current position:

The company makes and sells 600,000 units at a selling price of £40 per unit.

Proposed position:

The company is planning to increase the selling price to £50 per unit, and with an increased marketing budget position the product as a premium item. There will inevitably be a reduction in volume, but this will be partly offset by a reduction in stepped fixed production costs. The labour force has been working overtime to meet the current demand level and this will no longer be necessary.

The actual and forecast information is shown below.

	Current (Actual)	Proposed (Forecast)
Sales price per unit	£40	£50
Sales volume	600,000	500,000
	£	£
Revenue	24,000,000	25,000,000
Direct materials	4,800,000	4,000,000
Direct labour	7,200,000	5,000,000
Stepped fixed production costs	5,000,000	4,700,000
Total costs of sales	17,000,000	13,700,000
Gross profit	7,000,000	11,300,000
Marketing costs	3,000,000	5,000,000
Administration costs	2,000,000	2,000,000
Profit	2,000,000	4,300,000
Direct material cost per unit	£8.00	£8.00
Direct labour cost per unit	£12.00	£10.00
Stepped fixed production cost per unit	£8.33	£9.40
Marketing cost per unit	£5.00	£10.00
Gross profit margin	29.17%	45.20%
Profit margin	8.33%	17.20%
Inventory of finished goods	£2,125,000	
Trade receivables	£4,000,000	

Draft a report for the Finance Director covering the following:

An explanation of the change in gross profit margin from the actual to the proposed position, referring to the following:

·   sales price

·   direct material cost

·   direct labour cost

·   stepped fixed production costs

An explanation of what is likely to happen to the current asset requirements of the business by considering:

·   the expected inventory levels based on the current holding period

·   the expected trade receivables levels based on the current collection period

Report

To: Finance Director

From: Accounting Technician

Date: Today

Subject: Proposed Position

Change in Gross Profit Margin:

Sales Price

Direct material cost

Direct labour cost

Stepped fixed production costs

Current Asset Requirements:

Inventory levels

Trade receivable levels

Practice assessment 3

Task 1

The following information has been provided related to the production of Quintox.

·   Fixed overheads are absorbed on a per unit basis.

·   The budgeted output per month is 500,000 units of Quintox.

·   During December there was over-absorption of fixed overheads of £25,000.

·   Actual fixed overheads in December amounted to £551,000.

·   The actual output of Quintox in December was 480,000 units.

Calculate the information required to complete the following table:

Fixed overhead absorbed in December	£
Fixed overhead absorption rate per unit	£
Budgeted total fixed overheads per month	£

Task 2

Classy Glass Limited manufactures sealed triple-glazed units for new energy-efficient houses.

The company operates a standard cost system in which:

- Purchases of materials are recorded at standard cost

- Direct material and direct labour costs are variable

- Production overheads are fixed and absorbed on a labour hour basis

The budgeted activity and actual results for the month of March are as follows:

	Budget		Actual	
Production (sealed units)		2,500		2,650
Direct materials (glass)	7,500 sq m	£52,500	8,000 sq m	£57,000
Direct labour	2,500 hours	£37,500	2,800 hours	£42,000
Fixed overheads		£75,000		£74,000
Total cost		£165,000		£173,000

(a) Calculate the following variances (if any) for March:

Variance	£	A/F
Direct material price variance		
Direct material usage variance		
Direct labour rate variance		
Direct labour efficiency variance		

(b) It has been revealed that the direct labour force is not yet fully trained. It is estimated that this would account for each unit taking 5% longer than standard to manufacture.

Calculate the part of the direct labour efficiency variance related to training, and the part that may be due to other factors.

Variance	£	A/F
Part of direct labour efficiency variance due to incomplete training		
Part of direct labour efficiency variance due to other factors		

Task 3

You have been provided with the following information regarding fixed overheads:

Budgeted fixed overheads	£600,000
Fixed overhead absorption base	Direct labour hours
Budgeted output	300,000 units
Standard labour hours per unit	0.2 hours
Actual output	285,000 units
Actual labour hours	55,000 hours
Actual fixed overheads	£612,000

Calculate the following information and insert the figures into the table.

	£	A / F
Fixed overhead absorption rate per direct labour hour		
Fixed overhead expenditure variance		
Fixed overhead absorbed by actual production		
Fixed overhead volume variance		
Fixed overhead capacity variance		
Fixed overhead efficiency variance		

Task 4

A company uses standard marginal costing to monitor and control its costs. The company's only product is milk which is purchased in bulk and sold in 2 litre bottles. The milk, bottles and direct labour are all variable costs. Fixed overheads are the only fixed costs.

The following budgetary control report has been provided:

	Budget		Actual	
Production (bottles)		4,000,000		3,950,000
Milk	8,000,000 litres	£3,200,000	7,905,000 litres	£3,122,500
Bottles	4,000,000 units	£60,000	3,950,800 units	£60,100
Direct labour	2,000 hours	£36,000	2,000 hours	£36,500
Fixed overheads		£400,000		£401,500
Total costs		£3,696,000		£3,620,600

The following variances have been calculated:

Direct materials (milk) price	£39,500	F
Direct materials (milk) usage	£2,000	
Direct materials (bottles) price	£838	
Direct materials (bottles) usage	£12	A
Direct labour rate	£500	
Direct labour efficiency	£450	A
Fixed overhead expenditure	£1,500	

Complete the marginal costing operating statement on the next page.

Budgeted/standard variable cost for actual production			£
Budgeted fixed costs			£
Variances:	**Favourable £**	**Adverse £**	
Direct materials (milk) price			
Direct materials (milk) usage			
Direct materials (bottles) price			
Direct materials (bottles) usage			
Direct labour rate			
Direct labour efficiency			
Fixed overhead expenditure			
Total variance			£
Actual cost of actual production			£

Task 5

(a)   The following data relates to the prices per kilogram of a type of fruit. Complete the table by inserting the seasonal variations, including + or − signs.

	March	April	May
Actual price	£1.30	£1.25	£1.10
Trend	£1.28	£1.30	£1.32
Seasonal variation			

(b)   A formula has been developed to estimate the future trend in vehicle prices.

It is based on the equation $y = mx + c$, where

y is the expected price for a specific type of vehicle in the future

m is a constant £25

x is the month number of the required future date, counting from the base month of January 2012 (ie January 2012 is month 0)

c is a constant £14,000

Calculate the expected vehicle price in October 2014.

£ _____

(c)   Calculate the 3 month moving averages for the following sales volume data:

Month	Sales volume	3 month moving average
January	57,000	
February	58,000	
March	57,500	
April	60,000	
May	61,000	
June	60,500	
July	63,000	

Task 6

Performance Assemblies Limited reconditions and tunes vehicle engines for sale to the motor trade.

The company uses two grades of direct labour. Grade L employees are paid a basic £13 per hour and normally carry out the basic assembly of the reconditioned engines. Grade H employees are those who have been promoted from grade L and given further training to enable them to carry out the more advanced assembly work together with engine tuning. Grade H employees are paid a basic £17 per hour. Both grades of employee are paid a 50% premium rate for any overtime, and this is incorporated into the actual direct labour cost. The standard hourly rates have been set at £14 for grade L and £18 for grade H employees to allow for a small amount of premium rate pay.

During the month of May the following variances were recorded.

Variance	Favourable £	Adverse £
Direct labour (Grade L) efficiency	7,700	
Direct labour (Grade L) rate	1,450	
Direct labour (Grade H) efficiency		9,000
Direct labour (Grade H) rate		3,875

You have discovered the following additional information regarding the May results.

· The standard labour hours for the actual output during May was 2,000 hours of grade L labour plus 2,000 hours of grade H labour.

· Several grade L employees were sick during May.

· No grade L employees worked any overtime in May.

· Several grade H employees agreed to carry out duties normally carried out by grade L employees during May. This was in addition to their normal hours, and increased their usual amount of overtime hours.

Using this information, prepare a report for the Production Director providing an explanation of each variance together with possible reasons for each variance (including numerical information where possible).

Direct Labour Variances for May – Explanations and Possible Reasons

- Direct labour (Grade L) efficiency variance

- Direct labour (Grade L) rate variance

- Direct labour (Grade H) efficiency variance

- Direct labour (Grade H) rate variance

Task 7

Eye Limited is comparing its results with its major competitor Jay plc. You have been given the following information about Eye and Jay for the year just ended.

Statement of Profit or Loss	Eye	Jay
	£000	£000
Turnover	36,000	57,200
Cost of production		
Direct (raw) materials	8,000	13,650
Direct labour	7,200	11,375
Fixed production overheads	5,000	9,000
Total cost of production	20,200	34,025
Gross profit	**15,800**	**23,175**
Selling and distribution costs	4,000	7,100
Administration costs	3,250	4,800
Advertising costs	4,200	5,500
Net profit	**4,350**	**5,775**

Other information		Eye	Jay
Number of units sold	Units	4,000,000	6,500,000
Net assets	(£000)	65,000	95,000

Calculate the performance indicators to complete the following table for Eye Ltd and Jay plc:

Give answers to two decimal places.

	Eye Ltd	Jay plc
Selling price per unit		
Direct material cost per unit		
Direct labour cost per unit		
Fixed production overheads per unit		
Gross profit margin		
Net profit margin		
Administration cost as % of turnover		
Return on net assets		

Task 8

Tripro Limited manufactures three products, the Uno, Duo and Trio. The following statement shows the draft budget for the following three months.

	Uno	Duo	Trio	Total
Sales (units)	200,000	150,000	250,000	
	£	£	£	£
Sales Revenue	2,000,000	750,000	3,000,000	5,750,000
Materials	500,000	250,000	1,250,000	2,000,000
Labour	400,000	400,000	400,000	1,200,000
Overheads	300,000	300,000	300,000	900,000
Profit / (Loss)	800,000	(200,000)	1,050,000	1,650,000

You have established the following facts about the business.

· The same type of material is used for each product, at a cost of £10 per kilo.

· The products are made in one factory.

· The employees are all paid a fixed salary, and are on annual contracts which have just been renewed. The total labour cost is apportioned in the budget evenly over the three products.

· The overheads are a fixed cost which has been spread evenly over the three products in the budget.

The material supplier has just notified the company that the supply will be restricted in the next three months to 150,000 kilos. Tripro Limited does not hold any inventory of this material.

Draft a revised budget using the following format that maximises the profit that can be achieved based on the restricted volume of raw material.

	Uno	Duo	Trio	Total
Sales (units)				
	£	£	£	£
Sales Revenue				
Materials				
Contribution				
Labour				
Overheads				
Profit				

Task 9

Star Assemblies Limited is considering installing a new boiler system in its factory to provide heating and power.

Details are as follows:

- The existing boiler system will cost £8,000 to remove, and has no value. If retained, the existing boiler system has an expected life of a further 5 years.

- The new boiler system will cost £57,000 including installation.

- The current boiler system costs £22,000 per year in energy, £8,000 per year in maintenance and £2,000 per year in depreciation.

- The new boiler system would cost £12,000 per year in energy, cost nothing to maintain in the first two years (as it would be under guarantee) and £3,000 per year for the remaining life.

- The new boiler would be depreciated in the accounts on a straight line basis over the life of 5 years. There is no expected residual value.

- At the end of the 5 year period both old and new boiler systems would have the same cost of removal.

- The company's cost of capital is 10%, and this rate has been used for the discount factors in the table shown below.

- All annual costs can be assumed to occur in arrears.

(a) Complete the following table to calculate the net present value of the new system.

Year	Detail	Cash Flow £	Discount Factor	Present Value £
0	Initial costs	-57,000	1.000	-57,000
1	Net annual savings	8,600	0.909	7818
2		8,600	0.826	7104
3		5,600	0.751	4206
4		5,600	0.683	3825
5		5,600	0.621	3477
Net Present Value				-30,568

(b) Complete the following sentence.

The net present value of the scheme is **positive / negative**, so from a financial point of view the new boiler system is **worthwhile / not worthwhile**.

for your calculations:

Task 10

Vista Hotels Limited operates a number of small hotels. As part of its planning process it is considering following one of two scenarios for the next year.

Statement of Profit or Loss	Scenario 1 £	Scenario 2 £
Turnover	1,200,000	1,950,000
Variable costs		
Food	150,000	300,000
Laundry	105,000	210,000
Cleaning	180,000	300,000
Total variable costs	435,000	810,000
Contribution	**765,000**	**1,140,000**
Selling and marketing costs	100,000	450,000
Administration costs	350,000	350,000
Financial costs	130,000	130,000
Net profit	**185,000**	**210,000**

Other information

Number of room-nights occupied	15,000	30,000
Number of room-nights available	40,000	40,000

The first scenario is based on the current situation. The second scenario is based on using a combination of discounting and advertising with celebrity endorsement.

Draft a report to the Finance Director covering the following

· An explanation of why the contribution amounts are different

· An explanation of why the net profit margins and amounts are different

· A recommendation, with reasons, as to which scenario to adopt

Report on Scenarios

- Contribution Amounts

- Net Profit Margins and Amounts

- Recommendation, with reasons

Practice assessment 1 answers

Task 1

(a)

1 unit of Exe	Quantity	Cost per unit £	Total cost £
Material	1.3	4.50	5.85
Labour	0.2	18.00	3.60
Fixed costs	0.2	10.00	2.00
Total			11.45

(b)   The standard quantity of material for each unit is 0.2 kg

Task 2

(a)   (a)   £720 Favourable

(b)   (c)   £800 Adverse

(c)   (c)   £125,000

(d)   (b)   £3,300 Adverse

Task 3

(a)   The fixed overhead volume variance is **£20,000 favourable.**

The fixed overhead expenditure variance is **£15,000 adverse.**

(b)   The fixed overhead efficiency variance is **£2,700 adverse.**

The fixed overhead capacity variance is **£900 adverse.**

Task 4

	Favourable £	Adverse £	
Budgeted cost for actual production			£77,868
Variances:	**Favourable £**	**Adverse £**	
Direct materials (instant coffee) price		310	
Direct materials (instant coffee) usage		150	
Direct materials (glass jars) price	18		
Direct materials (glass jars) usage		8	
Direct labour rate	110		
Direct labour efficiency		252	
Fixed overhead expenditure		150	
Fixed overhead volume	300		
Total variances	428	870	£442
Actual cost of actual production			£78,310

Task 5

(a)   The trend in prices is an **increase** of **£0.60** per month.

(b)   (d)   106

(c)   (b)   The cost index in April was 122 and the decrease from January to April is 2.4%

Task 6

Report	
To: Production Director	From: Accounting technician
Date: xx	Subject: Report on September production of strawberry yoghurt

There were three significant material variances.

Price Variances

• Explanation and reasons

The only significant price variance was an adverse variance of £30,000 relating to the price of strawberries. This appears to have been caused by the poor UK weather which increased the buying price from the standard 50p per kg to an average 60p per kg. The actual quantity of strawberries used per pot was 150 grams (as identified below under 'Usage Variances'), therefore the actual quantity used in 2 million pots was 300,000 kilos. This accounts for the price variance of £30,000.

• Future strategies

Although such price changes caused by weather conditions are difficult to avoid, the buyer could consider sourcing fruit from outside the UK if necessary. This would however have transport cost implications and would have to be considered carefully so as not to damage our relationships with our current suppliers.

Usage Variances

• Explanation and reasons

There was an adverse usage variance of £50,000 for strawberries, and a favourable usage variance of £20,000 for yoghurt. Both these variances relate to the malfunction of the filling equipment.

It seems from the data that the equipment filled each 500 gram pot with an average of 350 grams of yoghurt and 150 grams of strawberries. The additional 50 grams of strawberries at the standard price of 50p per kilo for the 2 million pots accounts for the £50,000 variance. The favourable variance for the reduced amount of yoghurt is lower at £20,000 since the yoghurt is cheaper at a standard 20p per kilo.

Although this malfunction would not have created any legal issues since the fruit content was well above the minimum stated on the pots, we have incurred additional net costs of £30,000.

• Future strategies

Urgent consideration should be given to regular quality checks on the output of all the production lines (for example hourly). This could be carried out using sampling to analyse the content of the output so that any equipment malfunction is quickly noticed and action taken. Simply weighing each pot is not sufficient, since this does not detect a problem of the kind that has occurred in September.

If you require any further information, please contact me.

Task 7

	Cosy	Lush
Selling price per room-night	£75.00	£70.00
Occupancy rate (%)	50.00%	80.00%
Variable costs per room-night	£40.00	£35.00
Contribution per room-night	£35.00	£35.00
Contribution / sales ratio (%)	46.67%	50.00%
Net profit margin	5.52%	12.44%
Selling and marketing cost as % of turnover	22.86%	20.83%

Task 8

(a)

	Units	Price/cost £	Total £
Additional revenue	3,000,000	0.10	300,000
Savings on materials	3,000,000	0.15	450,000
Reduction in selling and distribution costs			150,000
Additional depreciation			(400,00)
Additional annual profit			500,000

(b)

Return on additional investment (%)	12.5%
Total fixed costs	£1,350,000
Contribution per unit	£1.35
Break even sales volume in units	1,000,000
Margin of safety (%)	66.67%

Task 9

(a)

	£
Sales price per unit	30.00
Profit margin	12.00
Total costs	18.00
Fixed cost per unit	9.00
Material cost per unit	4.00
Maximum labour cost per unit	5.00
Target labour time per unit (minutes)	20

(b)   The Trade Union negotiator wished to increase the hourly labour rate by 6%. He believes that in return, employees can produce each unit in 18 minutes if they are provided with additional training. If achievable, this proposal should be **accepted** because it **reduces** the labour cost per unit. The labour cost under this proposal would be **£4.77** per unit.

Task 10

Report

To: Finance Director   Subject: Scenarios 1 & 2

From: Accounting technician   Date: xx

(a)   Why are the gross profit margins different?

- Sales Price / Sales Volume

  Although the sales volume in scenario 2 is 50% greater than in scenario 1, this itself does not affect the gross profit margin (as a percentage). As noted later the increased volume does however spread the fixed costs over more units. The margin is affected by the selling price which is £2 per unit less in scenario 2. This has the effect of reducing the gross profit margin as a percentage.

- Materials

  The material cost is the same per unit in each scenario, since it behaves as a variable cost. This therefore has no impact on the gross profit margin.

- Labour

  The labour cost per unit is slightly higher when the volume is greater. This could be due (for example) to the use of overtime working. The impact on the gross profit margin is to reduce it slightly in scenario 2.

- Fixed production costs

  The fixed production costs form a large part of the cost of production. Since the volume is much higher in scenario 2, the fixed production cost per unit is significantly lower. This has the effect of improving the gross profit margin, and is the main factor in the difference between the margins. It more than compensates for the impact of selling price and labour costs.

(b)   Why are the operating profit margins different?

The operating profit margin in scenario 2 is influenced by the gross profit margin which is better than that in scenario 1, as discussed above. It also benefits from selling and distribution costs that appear to be semi-variable, and administration costs that behave as a fixed cost.

(c)   Recommendation, with reasons, as to which course of action to take

Provided the situation outlined in scenario 2 is thought to be achievable, then this should be followed, since it provides more than twice the operating profit of scenario 1. This is due to the economies of scale that impact on the fixed costs within the business.

However, before finalising a decision, particular care should be taken to examine the sales units forecast under scenario 2, because if this is flawed then the selling price reduction could easily lead to a worse operating profit than in scenario 1.

Practice
assessment 2
answers

Task 1

(a)	Standard quantity of labour per unit (in minutes)	12 minutes
(b)	Budgeted quantity of materials to produce 27,000 units (in kilos)	60,750 kilos
(c)	Budgeted quantity of labour to produce 27,000 units (in hours)	5,400 hours
(d)	Budgeted labour cost to produce 27,000 units (in £)	£48,600
(e)	Budgeted overhead absorption rate per unit (in £)	£3.00
(f)	Amount of over absorption of fixed overheads (in £)	£3,500

Workings:

(a) 5,000 hours / 25,000 units x 60

(b) 56,250 kilos / 25,000 units x 27,000 units

(c) 5,000 hours / 25,000 units x 27,000 units

(d) £45,000 / 25,000 units x 27,000 units

(e) £75,000 / 25,000 units

(f) (27,000 units x £3) – £77,500

Task 2

(a)   The standard cost per kilogram is **£1.35.**

Working: (£10,250 – £260) / 7,400 kilograms

(b)   The material usage variance is **£1,250 adverse.**

Working:

Standard usage:

(9,950 units x 180,000 litres / 12,000 units) = 149,250 litres

Standard price:

£225,000 / 180,000 litres = £1.25 per litre

Material usage variance:

(149,250 – 150,250) litres x £1.25 = £1,250 adverse

(c)   The labour efficiency variance is **£350 favourable** (excluding idle time).

The idle time variance is **£1,120 adverse.**

Workings:

Standard time for actual output:

3,000 hours x 25,000 units / 24,000 units = 3,125 hours

Labour efficiency variance:

(3,125 – 3,100) hours x £14 = £350 favourable

Idle time variance:

(3,100 – 3,180) hours x £14 = £1,120 adverse

Task 3

(a)   The fixed overhead volume variance is **£9,000 favourable**.

The actual fixed production overheads incurred were **£153,000**.

Workings:

Fixed overhead absorption rate:

£157,500 / 35,000 units = £4.50 per unit

Fixed overhead volume variance:

(37,000 units – 35,000 units) x £4.50 = £9,000 favourable

Actual fixed production overheads incurred:

£157,500 – £4,500 (favourable expenditure variance) = £153,000

(b)

Variance	Amount £	Adverse / Favourable
Fixed overhead capacity	11,700	Favourable
Fixed overhead efficiency	3,900	Favourable

Workings:

Fixed overhead absorption rate:

£107,250 / 5,500 hours = £19.50 per standard labour hour

Standard hours for actual production:

63,000 x (5,500 / 55,000) = 6,300 standard hours

Fixed overhead capacity variance:

(6,100 hours – 5,500 hours) x £19.50 = £11,700 favourable

Fixed overhead efficiency variance:

(6,300 hours – 6,100 hours) x £19.50 = £3,900 favourable

Task 4

Budgeted variable cost for actual production			£40,420
Budgeted fixed cost			£190,000
Total budgeted cost for actual production			£230,420
Variance	**Favourable £**	**Adverse £**	
Direct material price	896		
Direct material usage		638	
Direct labour rate		225	
Direct labour efficiency		320	
Variable overhead expenditure	450		
Variable overhead efficiency		400	
Fixed overhead expenditure		5,000	
Total variance	1,346	6,583	+£5,237
Actual cost of actual production			£235,657

Working:

Budgeted variable cost for actual production:

(£22,040 + £6,080 + £7,600) x 21,500 units / 19,000 units = £40,420

Task 5

(a)

	Amount
Price per tonne based on August index (to nearest penny)	£534.59
Part of variance explained by change in index (to nearest £)	£1,244
Part of variance not explained by change in index (to nearest £)	£2,956
	%
Percentage reduction in index (to two decimal places)	1.00

Workings:

Price per tonne based on August index:

£540 x 187.6 / 189.5 = £534.59

Original variance:

(230 tonnes x £540) – £120,000 = £4,200 favourable

Sub variance explained by change in index:

(230 tonnes x £540) – (230 tonnes x £534.59) = £1,244

Sub variance not explained by change in index:

(230 tonnes x £534.59) – £120,000 = £2,956

Percentage reduction in index:

(189.5 – 187.6) / 189.5 x 100 = 1.00%

(b)

	October	November
Cost per kilo	£540.62	£542.96

Working:

Cost is increasing each month by £2.34.

(c)   The forecast cost per tonne in December 20X4 is **£3,670.40** to the nearest penny.

Working:

(44.1 x 29) + 2,391.5 = £3,670.40

Task 6

> **Direct Labour Variances**
>
> Several direct labour variances can be calculated to help us compare the actual costs of direct labour with the expected costs. The total direct labour variance provides us with an overall comparison, and this can then be split into a rate variance and an efficiency variance.
>
> Before we can calculate the total direct labour variance we need to work out what the expected (or budgeted) cost of labour is for the actual output that was achieved. We cannot make a fair comparison with the actual cost if the expected cost is based on a different output level. To do this we 'flex' the budgeted figures.
>
> Using the figures given, we can see that if the budgeted labour cost for producing 40,000 units is £320,000, then the budgeted labour cost for producing 43,000 units (the actual production) will be £320,000 x 43,000 / 40,000 = £344,000.
>
> We now have the ingredients to calculate the total direct labour variance, by comparing the expected cost of £344,000 with the actual cost of £343,440. This gives us a difference (called a variance) of £560. Because the actual cost was lower than expected we call this variance a 'favourable' one.
>
> We can now move on to divide this variance into two sub-variances. The first is the direct labour rate variance. This tells us how much difference in labour cost there is because the expected hourly rate wasn't paid. We can work out that the expected (or standard) hourly rate was £16 per hour by dividing the original budgeted cost by the budgeted hours (£320,000 / 20,000). If all the actual 21,200 hours had been paid at £16 per hour the labour cost would have been 21,200 x £16 = £339,200. Since the actual cost of these 21,200 hours was £343,440, the difference of £343,440 − £339,200 gives us the direct labour rate variance of £4,240. This time it's an adverse variance because the actual cost was higher.
>
> Finally we can look at the other reason that the labour costs were different from those expected – the time it took to carry out the work. The variance that we can use to show this is called the efficiency variance. We can calculate that if it should take 20,000 hours to produce 40,000 units, then it should take 20,000 x 43,000 / 40,000 = 21,500 hours to make the 43,000 units that were produced. Remember that it actually took 21,200 hours. Since we have already looked at the differences caused by the actual rate being paid, we can simply value this difference in hours of 21,500 − 21,200 = 300 hours at the standard hourly rate. The direct labour efficiency variance is therefore 300 hours x £16 = £4,800 favourable (the time taken was less than expected).
>
> In summary, the total labour cost variance was £560 favourable. By calculating the sub variances we can see that the actual cost was higher due to paying more than the standard rate – the rate variance was £4,240 adverse. Set against this is the cost of the time saved which gives us the efficiency variance of £4,800 favourable. We can see that £4,800 minus £4,240 equals the total variance of £560.

Task 7

(a)

	Scenario 1	Scenario 2
Return on net assets	12.50%	22.86%
Inventory holding period in days	47.91	66.54
Sales price per unit	£22.00	£27.00
Marginal (variable) cost per unit	£16.00	£16.00

Workings:	Scenario 1	Scenario 2
Return on net assets:	£200,000 / £1,600,000 %	£320,000 / £1,400,000 %
Inventory holding: Variable cost of sales	£4,400,000 – £1,200,000 = £3,200,000	£3,240,000 – £1,320,000 = £1,920,000
	£420,000 / £3,200,000 x 365 = 47.91	£350,000 / £1,920,000 x 365 = 66.54
Sales price per unit:	£4,400,000 / 200,000	£3,240,000 / 120,000
Marginal cost per unit:	£3,200,000 / 200,000	£1,920,000 / 120,000

(b)

	Scenario 3
Net assets	£1,800,000
Contribution to sales ratio	50%
Fixed costs	£1,000,000
Return on net assets	10%
Profit (£)	£180,000
Contribution (£)	£1,180,000
Sales Revenue (£)	£2,360,000

Workings:

Profit:	£1,800,000 x 10% = £180,000
Contribution:	£180,000 + £1,000,000 = £1,180,000
Sales Revenue:	£1,180,000 / 50%

(c)   (d)   Revenue / Net assets

Task 8

(a)

	Product Toll	Product Tall
Contribution per unit	£240	£230
Contribution per kilogram of material	£40	£115
Priority ranking (1 or 2)	2	1
Number of units to be made to maximise profit	3,500	4,500
Total contribution for each product based on above numbers	£840,000	£1,035,000

Workings:

	Product Toll	**Product Tall**
Contribution per unit	£700 – £300 – £160	£500 – £100 – £170
Contribution per kilo	£240 / 6	£230 / 2

Produce maximum units of Product Tall (4,500), using up 9,000 kilos of material. Remainder of material (21,000 kg) used to make 3,500 units of Product Toll.

Total contribution	3,500 x £240	4,500 x £230

(b)   The price paid per kilogram for additional material must be less than **£90** to be worthwhile.

Working:

The additional material would be used to make additional units of Product Toll after above decision. Contribution per kilogram is £40, added to original material cost of £50 means new cost must be less than £90 to make any contribution.

Task 9

(a)

	Selling price £25	Selling price £20
Estimated demand (units)	200,000	300,000
Target profit per unit	£6.25	£5.00
Target total costs per unit	£18.75	£15.00
Target fixed production costs per unit	£10.00	£8.00
Target variable costs per unit	£8.75	£7.00

Workings:

Target profit per unit	£25 x 25%	£20 x 25%
Target total costs per unit	£25 – £6.25	£20 – £5
Target fixed production costs per unit	£2,000,000 / 200,000 units	£2,400,000 / 300,000 units
Target variable costs per unit	£18.75 – £10	£15 – £8

(b)   A selling price of **£25** per unit would allow for target variable costs within the expected range.

Task 10

Report

To: Finance Director

From: Accounting Technician

Date: Today

Subject: Proposed Position

Change in Gross Profit Margin:

Sales Price

The change in sales price from £40 to £50 has an important impact on the improved gross profit margin under the proposal. The extra £10 per unit created by this change is reflected in an increased amount of gross profit per unit, and also increases the gross profit margin by £10 / £50 = 20%.

Direct material cost

The direct material cost per unit is unchanged at £8 per unit. This cost therefore acts entirely as a variable cost and has no impact on the gross profit margin.

Direct labour cost

The direct labour cost per unit reduces from £12 to £10. This is likely to be as a result of overtime working at premium rates no longer being required. This will help improve the gross profit margin.

Stepped fixed production costs

The stepped fixed production costs will reduce in total under the proposal by £300,000. However this is an increase in cost per unit since the costs are spread over fewer units. Although this will have a negative impact on the gross profit margin, it is heavily outweighed by the additional profit derived from the sales price change.

Current Asset Requirements:

Inventory levels

The current inventory level (based on total costs of sales) represents £2,125,000 / £17,000,000 x 365 = 45.6 days. If this were replicated under the proposed position the inventory valuation would be 45.6 / 365 x £13,700,000 = £1,712,000 approximately. This would reduce the current asset requirements by £413,000 if it were achieved.

Trade receivable levels

The current collection period is £4m / £24m x 365 = 60.8 days. The equivalent trade receivables under the proposal would be 60.8 / 365 x £25m = £4,164,000 approximately. This would increase the current asset requirements by approximately £164,000.

Taken together the impact of inventory and trade receivables would be to reduce the requirement for current assets by about £250,000.

Practice assessment 3 answers

Task 1

Fixed overhead absorbed in December	£576,000
Fixed overhead absorption rate per unit	£1.20
Budgeted total fixed overheads per month	£600,000

Workings:

Fixed overheads absorbed in December:

Actual overheads £551,000 + Over-absorption £25,000 = £576,000

Fixed overhead absorption rate per unit:

Fixed overheads absorbed £576,000 ÷ Actual units produced 480,000 = £1.20

Budgeted total fixed overheads per month:

Budgeted output per month 500,000 units x Absorption rate £1.20 = £600,000

Task 2

(a)

Variance	£	A/F
Direct material price variance	1,000	A
Direct material usage variance	350	A
Direct labour rate variance	0	
Direct labour efficiency variance	2,250	A

Workings:

Direct materials price variance:

$(8,000 \text{ sq m} \times £7^*) - £57,000 = £1,000 \text{ A}$

*£52,500 / 7,500 sq m

Direct materials usage variance:

$((2,650 \times 3 \text{ sq m}^*) - 8,000 \text{ sq m}) \times £7 = £350 \text{ A}$

*7,500 sq m / 2,500 units

Direct labour rate variance:

$(2,800 \times £15^*) - £42,000 = £0$

*£37,500 / 2,500 hours

Direct labour efficiency variance:

$((2,650 \text{ units} \times 1 \text{ hour per unit}) - 2,800 \text{ hours}) \times £15 = £2,250 \text{ A}$

(b)

Variance	£	A/F
Part of direct labour efficiency variance due to incomplete training	1,987.50	A
Part of direct labour efficiency variance due to other factors	262.50	A

Workings:

Revised time to make 2,650 units:

2,650 x 1.05 hours = 2,782.5 hours

Direct labour efficiency variance due to training:

$(2,650 \text{ hours} - 2,782.5 \text{ hours}) \times £15 = £1,987.50 \text{ A}$

Direct labour efficiency variance due to other factors:

$(2,782.5 \text{ hours} - 2,800 \text{ hours}) \times £15 = £262.50 \text{ A}$

Task 3

	£	A / F
Fixed overhead absorption rate per direct labour hour	10	
Fixed overhead expenditure variance	12,000	A
Fixed overhead absorbed by actual production	570,000	
Fixed overhead volume variance	30,000	A
Fixed overhead capacity variance	50,000	A
Fixed overhead efficiency variance	20,000	F

Workings:

Fixed overhead absorption rate per direct labour hour:
£600,000 / (300,000 units x 0.2 hours) = £10

Fixed overhead expenditure variance:
£600,000 – £612,000 = £12,000 A

Fixed overhead absorbed by actual production:
Standard hours for actual production: 285,000 units x 0.2 = 57,000 hours
Overhead absorbed: 57,000 hours x £10 = £570,000

Fixed overhead volume variance:
£570,000 – £600,000 = £30,000 A

Fixed overhead capacity variance:
(55,000 x £10) – £600,000 = £50,000 A

Fixed overhead efficiency variance:
£570,000 – £550,000 = £20,000 F

Task 4

Budgeted/standard variable cost for actual production			£3,254,800
Budgeted fixed costs			£400,000
Variances:	**Favourable £**	**Adverse £**	
Direct materials (milk) price	39,500		
Direct materials (milk) usage		2,000	
Direct materials (bottles) price		838	
Direct materials (bottles) usage		12	
Direct labour rate		500	
Direct labour efficiency		450	
Fixed overhead expenditure		1,500	
Total variance	34,200		−£34,200
Actual cost of actual production			£3,620,600

Workings:

Budgeted / Standard variable cost for actual production:

(£3,200,000 + £60,000 + £36,000) x 3,950,000 / 4,000,000 = £3,254,800

Task 5

(a)

	March	April	May
Actual price	£1.30	£1.25	£1.10
Trend	£1.28	£1.30	£1.32
Seasonal variation	+£0.02	−£0.05	−£0.22

(b)   **£14,825**

Working: y = (£25 x 33) + £14,000

(c)

Month	Sales volume	3 month moving average
January	57,000	
February	58,000	57,500
March	57,500	58,500
April	60,000	59,500
May	61,000	60,500
June	60,500	61,500
July	63,000	

Task 6

Direct Labour Variances for May – Explanations and Possible Reasons

- Direct labour (Grade L) efficiency variance

  The labour efficiency variance is the result of more or fewer hours being taken than the standard number for the output. The difference in hours is valued at the standard hourly rate. In this case the variance of £7,700 favourable means that 550 fewer hours than the standard 2,000 hours were worked, valued at the standard £14 per hour.

  This may have been caused by the absence of some grade L workers during May, whose work was then undertaken by grade H employees.

- Direct labour (Grade L) rate variance

  The labour rate variance shows the increased or reduced cost of the actual hours worked due to paying a rate that differs from standard. Here the actual 1,450 hours worked have cost £1,450 less than if they had been paid at the standard rate of £14 per hour. This means that the actual rate was the basic £13 per hour, which agrees with the fact that there was no overtime premium rates paid to this level of employees during May.

- Direct labour (Grade H) efficiency variance

  The adverse efficiency variance of £9,000 for grade H employees is a reflection of the increased number of hours worked during May compared to standard. This equates to an additional 500 hours at the standard rate of £18 per hour. It is likely that this is mainly due to grade H employees undertaking work normally carried out by grade L employees. However if we examine the total hours worked by both grades we find that 1,450 + 2,500 = 3,950 hours were worked, which is slightly fewer than the 4,000 standard hours. This could possibly be due to the higher grade employees working more quickly on the lower level work.

- Direct labour (Grade H) rate variance

  The adverse variance of £3,875 relates to the additional cost of paying the actual hours at an average rate that is higher than the standard £18 per hour. This is probably due to the overtime premium rate that was paid during May so that grade H employees could carry out the additional work normally carried out by grade L employees. If more overtime than normal is worked the proportion of hours paid at the higher rate of £25.50 will be greater, increasing the labour cost.

Task 7

	Eye Ltd	Jay plc
Selling price per unit	£9.00	£8.80
Direct material cost per unit	£2.00	£2.10
Direct labour cost per unit	£1.80	£1.75
Fixed production overheads per unit	£1.25	£1.38
Gross profit margin	43.89%	40.52%
Net profit margin	12.08%	10.10%
Administration cost as % of turnover	9.03%	8.39%
Return on net assets	6.69%	6.08%

Task 8

	Uno	Duo	Trio	Total
Sales (units)	200,000	150,000	150,000	
	£	£	£	£
Sales Revenue	2,000,000	750,000	1,800,000	4,550,000
Materials	500,000	250,000	750,000	1,500,000
Contribution	1,500,000	500,000	1,050,000	3,050,000
Labour				1,200,000
Overheads				900,000
Profit				950,000

Workings:

Priority should be given to the products with the highest contribution per kilo of raw material. This is calculated as follows:

	Uno	Duo	Trio
Contribution			
(Sales revenue – materials)	£1,500,000	£500,000	£1,750,000
Materials required (kilos)	50,000	25,000	125,000
Contribution per kilo	£30	£20	£14

Therefore priority should be given to Uno and Duo, with the balance of available material being used to make Trios. Each unit of Trio requires 0.5 kilos of material (125,000 kilos / 250,000 units). The remaining 75,000 kilos of material now available is enough to make 75,000 / 0.5 = 150,000 units of Trio.

Task 9

(a)

Year	Detail	Cash Flow £	Discount Factor	Present Value £
0	Initial costs	−65,000	1.000	−65,000
1	Net annual savings	18,000	0.909	16,362
2		18,000	0.826	14,868
3		15,000	0.751	11,265
4		15,000	0.683	10,245
5		15,000	0.621	9,315
Net Present Value				−2,945

Workings:

Initial costs £57,000 + £8,000 removal of old system = £65,000

Net annual savings – years 1 and 2:
Energy £22,000 – £12,000; Maintenance £8,000 – £0; Depreciation ignored as non-cash item. Total annual savings £18,000

Net annual savings – years 3 to 5:
Energy £22,000 – £12,000; Maintenance £8,000 – £3,000; Depreciation ignored as non-cash item. Total annual savings £15,000

(b)   The net present value of the scheme is **negative**, so from a financial point of view the new boiler system is **not worthwhile**.

Task 10

Report on Scenarios

- Contribution Amounts

The main reason for the difference in contributions is the pricing structure and anticipated room occupancy. The first scenario is based on an average price per room of £80 and an occupancy rate of 37.5%. The second scenario assumes a lower average price per room of £65, but a much higher occupancy rate of 75%. This increases the turnover of scenario 2 compared with scenario 1.

The variable costs of food and laundry are based on £10 and £7 per occupied room respectively under both scenarios. The cleaning cost per room is £12 under scenario 1, but reduced to £10 under scenario 2.

The combined impact of the above is a contribution amount under scenario 2 which is £375,000 greater than that shown in scenario 1.

- Net Profit Margins and Amounts

The net profits arise from the contributions less the fixed costs. The only difference in fixed costs is selling and marketing where the second scenario anticipates spending £350,000 more. This is the cost of increased advertising and celebrity endorsement which it is anticipated will double the occupancy rate when combined with the reduced room prices.

The net profit amount is higher under the second scenario, although as a percentage of turnover it is lower (10.77% compared with 15.42%).

- Recommendation, with reasons

Although the second scenario anticipates a higher net profit than scenario 1, it is only by a fairly small £25,000 difference. The second scenario relies on doubling room occupancy to 75%, and is therefore a more risky strategy. If this level of increased occupancy was not achieved there is scope for significantly reduced profit or even losses. The first scenario in contrast is based on current performance which is known to be achievable.

The recommendation is therefore to follow scenario 1.

for your notes

for your notes

for your notes

for your notes

for your notes

for your notes